SEEING THROUGH
THE EYES
OF ANOTHER

SEEING THROUGH THE EYES OF ANOTHER

Stories for seeing life from different perspectives

LARS COLLMAR
Translated by Lesley Gleeson

HINTON HOUSE

First published in 2010 by
Hinton House Publishers Ltd, Newman House, 4 High Street,
Buckingham, MK18 1NT, UK
T +44 (0)1280 822557 F +44 (0) 560 3135274
E info@hintonpublishers.co.uk

www.hintonpublishers.co.uk

British Library Cataloguing in Publication Data
Collmar, Lars, 1939–
    Seeing through the eyes of another. – (Stories for seeing
life from different perspectives ; v. 2)
    1. Social perception–Study and teaching (Secondary)
    2. Social perception–Testing.
    I. Title II. Series
    370.1'14-dc22

ISBN-13: 978 1 906531 25 6

Printed and bound in the United Kingdom

Original edition published in Swedish under the title *Två par ögon*
by Argument Förlag AB, Sweden.
© 2004 Argument Förlag AB och Lars Collmar

FSC
Mixed Sources
Product group from well-managed
forests and other controlled sources

Cert no. SA-COC-001530
www.fsc.org
© 1996 Forest Stewardship Council

Contents

Introduction

"Is that what really happened? I had no idea! If only I'd known I would have reacted completely differently."

How often do we rush to judge a person and their reactions to an event? Then later, when we learn more about the person and the situation we realise that the picture is much more complicated than we had originally thought. Many misunderstandings and conflicts could be avoided if only people took a little time to find out more about each other.

Seeing Through the Eyes of Another aims to stimulate and develop discussions which, it is hoped, will encourage and develop young people's ability to see things from different perspectives.

This resource depicts fourteen different everyday situations. Each chapter contains two stories describing the same event from two different perspectives. The stories are each followed by a set of questions designed to stimulate thought and discussion and then a third set of questions to answer after both stories have been read.

Each pair of stories addresses issues that are encountered in everyday life, and the questions that follow will stimulate lively group discussion and illuminate the perspectives and feelings of the characters involved.

Using *Seeing Through the Eyes of Another* should prove to be a fun and exciting challenge. Working with this material will help students to be more curious about what lies behind a situation, and instead of jumping

to conclusions they will begin to look for what might lie behind people's opinions, behaviour and reactions and this will encourage discussion instead of conflict.

This book is intended for use with young people aged twelve and upwards, with themes of some stories being more suited to younger students and some to those who are slightly older. However, all groups are different and this resource is flexible enough to be adapted as appropriate.

Suggestions for use

The stories in this resource can be used in whole-class groups, small group work or on a one-to-one basis.

Read one of the stories and then discuss the relevant questions. Now read the second story. Does the picture change? Discuss the questions relating to the second story and then the questions for both stories. It is not until both stories have been read that the complete picture is revealed.

Questions can be answered individually or used as a basis for groupwork and whole-group discussions. Groups could be divided into two and each given one of the stories to read and discuss. Each small group could then prepare answers the questions relating to their story for a whole-group presentation and discussion.

The major themes addressed in each set of stories are outlined below.

1 *Who Can You Trust?*: Trust, freedom, guilt, suspicion
2 *Abortion*: Abortion choices, communication, ethics
3 *Jump! Jump!*: Bullying, following the crowd, showing off, respect for others

Ideas for discussion & follow up

1 Discuss different situations where risks may arise if only half or a part of the truth is known.

- ◆ What might we do about this?
- ◆ Is it always necessary to know everything about a situation?
- ◆ When might we tell half-truths?
- ◆ In which situations might we do this consciously and when might we do it unconsciously?

- ◆ Can avoid half-truths or white lies really be avoided altogether?
- ◆ In what sort of situation might we be justified in not telling the whole truth?
- ◆ What could we do to make sure we always try to get the full picture?

2   An effective way of practising seeing a situation from different perspectives is to ask groups to write their own pairs of stories, describing the same situation with two different viewpoints, for example, two football players describing the same match. A third version could include the referee's point of view.

Examples:
>   Police officer – Demonstrator
>   Teacher – Pupil
>   Parent – Teenager
>   Girl – Boy

3   Another variant could be to ask the to group to write a description of a situation they've experienced together, or a film or a play they have all seen, even half an hour spent together at the school gates. Compare these stories. Do people emphasise different aspects of their experience and if so why?

4   Using some of the stories in this resource, ask members of the group to role-play the situations. How do they feel when taking the part of someone for whom they may not originally have had much sympathy?

The everyday issues covered in this book can be encountered at school, with families and friends and in relationships. This easy-to-use resource is ideal for use by teachers in PSHE discussions, and also by Speech and Language Therapists and other therapists addressing social and emotional development.

1 Who Can You Trust?

Josh's Story

Josh and his Dad had an unspoken agreement.

This is how it went. Josh was allowed to do more or less what he liked as long as he didn't do anything too stupid. The system relied on trust on both sides and so far things had worked out quite well.

It was good enough for Josh, he didn't trust people who felt they had to put everything into words and explain things at length. People who said "I trust you". Or "I love you". Or "I'll never leave you". It was almost like chanting a spell, he thought. As if they weren't really sure but hoped that if they said it out loud it would become true. If something really worked, it didn't need to be talked about, like trusting someone.

Josh seemed to have more freedom than most fourteen-year-old boys. He decided for himself what he did with his time. He slept when he was tired and got up when his alarm when off. He did his homework when he needed to, chatted on the internet or talked on the telephone whenever he felt like it. He came home when he decided he wanted to, although it was never particularly late. Sometimes he stayed the night at a friend's house or they stayed with him, but he always called home first.

It was also up to him whether or not he went to school. He did actually go most of the time, even when he wasn't feeling too well, because he enjoyed school, but if he sometimes felt too tired or wanted to stay at home and finish doing something then his Dad would ring the school and say he was ill.

Was this too much freedom for a fourteen year old? Well, everyone was happy, and it seemed to work. It wasn't as if his Dad didn't care about him, they would sit and talk until late at night about life and death, and love and hate, and religion and the state of the world, all the things a person needs to talk about with someone whose opinion they respect. No, it worked well.

Until tonight! Suddenly Dad started talking about things disappearing from home. First it was £20 that had been lying on top of the microwave, then a packet of cigarettes.

"Do you know anything about this, boys?"

Which meant "Did you take the money and the smokes?"

His younger brothers just seemed confused, but Josh was really insulted. How could Dad, who had started the day by asking who had taken his shoes, seriously suspect them of stealing, let alone smoking? Had he now managed to forget that he was really forgetful?

"I did throw out some rubbish this morning," Dad muttered. "But surely even I couldn't mistake a £20 note for an old envelope."

Josh smiled weakly. A friendly, but slightly pitying smile and then said, "I wouldn't be too sure of that."

"I saw the cigarettes near the cooker last night, and this morning they'd disappeared," Dad continued angrily.

"But you were looking for them yesterday morning too," said Josh tiredly. "Have you looked in your jacket pocket?"

Dad just became annoyed.

"The cigarettes have disappeared between last night and this morning. Exactly when isn't important. I know I didn't have them on me and anyway I've looked in all my pockets. So someone must have taken them. Does anyone know anything about this?"

The younger boys assured him that they'd neither stolen the money nor taken up smoking. Dad turned his eyes to Josh.

Josh smiled his pitying smile again. "All I can say is that I am completely innocent," he said casually, much more casually than he really felt.

"Then I'll just have to believe you," said Dad.

He sounded tired, and Josh could tell by his voice that he wasn't convinced.

"It's a shame he didn't insist," thought Josh. "Then I could have defended myself. Now I can't even do that."

"Hurry up and brush your teeth, and then get ready for bed," said Dad to the younger boys.

Josh went into his room.

He was so angry and disappointed. He felt ashamed even though he wasn't guilty. How could Dad even suspect him? He felt let down. He really doesn't know me at all, he thought. I thought Dad knew me well, but he really has no idea. And what can I do about it?

He felt really lonely.

Who Can You Trust?

Questions for Josh's story

1 Do you think the agreement between Josh and his Dad is a good one, or does Josh have more freedom than a fourteen-year-old is mature enough to cope with?

2 Josh doesn't think that important things in life, like trust or love, need to be discussed. Do you agree?

3 Can somebody feel embarrassed or ashamed even when they are not guilty?

4 Should Dad have mentioned the items that disappeared, or not?

5 Is it disappointing when you feel you can't quite trust someone you can normally rely on to do the right thing?

6 Why wasn't Dad convinced by Josh's answers? How could Josh have answered instead?

1 Who Can You Trust?

Dad's Story

Dad sat with the boys at tea time and felt really uncomfortable.

I must talk to them, he thought, otherwise I'm just being a coward. I know I put a £20 note on top of the microwave the other day, he said to himself. It was when I cleared out all the old letters from school, and the empty envelopes from the bills, and all those advertisements that swamp the house. They were all on top of the microwave. Could I really have thrown away a £20 note? It doesn't seem possible.

And then there was that packet of cigarettes. I know they were by the cooker only last night. (Or at least I think it was last night.) It was a new packet, and then this morning they were gone. It's simple, someone must have taken them, and if someone took the cigarettes then they took the money too.

This is wrong! I need to show the boys that I know what's going on.

Is it Josh? He's usually so sensible and trustworthy that I don't want to believe it. His school only ever has good things to say about him, but he is only fourteen, even if I like to think of him as a sensible adult. Has he had too much freedom and responsibility? Maybe he's just done this to get my attention, and anyway isn't it at about fourteen that kids start trying smoking? If not before…

Leo's only eleven, but I was about his age when I started pinching loose change from my Dad. Leo's much more impulsive than Josh ever was, and he does collect those action figures. Skeleton armies, the living dead and all that, he could quite easily put a hole in a £20 note if he felt like it.

And Sam is only six, so if he'd taken the money it would be more like a game to him. He has his strange little treasures hidden all over the house, small boxes hidden in the wardrobe and his sock drawer, which hold anything from foreign coins or shells to empty ink cartridges! His treasures. Yes, a real £20 note and a packet of cigarettes would be perfect treasure to hide.

It could be any of them, Dad thought tiredly.

It wasn't the actual theft that was the worst thing, all children take things at one time or other, until they learn better. And they're not really that old yet, not even Josh. But they have to understand that it doesn't pay to steal, that I will find out and that it poisons the whole atmosphere in the house when we can't trust each other.

Dad looked intently at his boys.

"Things have started to disappear round the house," he said. "First a £20 note and then an unopened packet of cigarettes, does anyone know anything about them?"

Leo just looked at him, and Sam said very seriously that he didn't smoke.

"No, the little ones are innocent enough," thought Dad. "I can still read them. Of course, they might have done it, but I'm pretty sure I'd able to tell."

What about Josh?

He suggested several places to start looking for the items, and when Dad gave him a challenging look he just smiled weakly.

"All I can say is that I am completely innocent," he said casually.

Dad wanted to shake him.

"Tell the truth," he wanted to say. "It doesn't matter if you did it but I need to know. I don't feel that I know you any more."

But of course he didn't say anything.

"Then I'll just have to believe you," he said instead, and felt really stupid.

It was time for the younger ones to get ready for bed and Josh disappeared into his room. He'd become so grown up lately, thought Dad. His friends know much more about what he's thinking and feeling than I do. I suppose that's how it should be, but it means that I don't know who he is any more.

Sometimes it makes me feel so sad.

Who can you trust?

Questions for Dad's story

1 Dad is nervous about talking to talk to the boys. Why do you think that is?

2 How do you think the money and the packet of cigarettes might have disappeared?

3 Do you think Josh took them just to get attention as his Dad suggests?

4 Dad thinks that all kids steal things at some time in their lives. Is this true?

5 Is it important for the family to find out how the money and cigarettes disappeared? Will it be possible to do so? What is the best way to go about it?

6 Was it a good or bad thing that Dad didn't shake Josh or shout at him, even when he felt like doing so?

Who can you trust?

Questions for both stories

1 Is Dad letting Josh down by suspecting him of stealing? Josh seems to think so.

2 What should you do if you are suspicious of someone you want to trust?

3 Is it possible to really know someone well, or do we just think we do? Can anyone really know what you think and feel?

4 Dad thinks it is probably right that Josh's friends know more about how Josh feels than he does. Do you agree?

5 If Josh was guilty, would this mean that he was a very different person from the one Dad believes he is?

6 What does it mean to trust someone?

7 Why does Dad suspect Josh more than the other boys?

Continued …

8 Both Josh and Dad feel sad and lonely. Why? Can anything be done about it?

9 Is this sort of loneliness the price we pay for being adults?

10 Suspecting someone you trust and being suspected of something both feel bad. How can Dad and the boys get rid of the tense atmosphere?

2 Abortion

Emily's Story

As always, the class were enjoying a serious debate. The subject was abortion. Should we really view a newly fertilized egg as a person with an obvious right to life? On the other hand do we ever have the right to end a life, however newly started? One side spoke – then the other, feelings were expressed here and others there, facts presented on one side and then the other.

Emily couldn't bear to listen. They didn't understand anything. Everyone was talking as if they were solving a difficult maths equation.

But Emily was pregnant.

Everything was different because it was happening to her.

Was she sure?

Yes, since yesterday. She'd finally plucked up the courage and gone to the other side of town to a chemist, and she'd bought a pregnancy test. The next morning, in the bathroom, she'd done the test. Positive!

The test could be unreliable early on in a pregnancy, according to the instruction leaflet. You might be pregnant even if the test was negative, but if it was positive, then you were pregnant. Always!

It felt strange that the test was positive already. The embryo was eighteen days, fourteen hours and about ten minutes old. She knew because it was on a Saturday night when she'd had sex for the first – and only – time. Stephen. (Should she say something to him? No, he mustn't find out!)

So, she was going to have a baby.

Except of course she wasn't. She was going to have an abortion. A girl of fourteen shouldn't have a baby. If the worst came to the worst she would have an abortion. That's just the way it was.

One boy in the class was saying quite firmly that a woman should have the right to decide what happened to her own body, at least for as long as the foetus was so undeveloped that it wouldn't know it was being aborted. Hmmm!

Another boy took over and spoke just as boldly about respecting life. A society that called itself humane should never forget to look after the weakest. Mmhmmm!

It was as if she'd joined a TV debate from outer space. What were they talking about? The only important thing here was that she was fourteen and she was pregnant.

Before now she would certainly have taken part in the discussion. What would she have said? It was strange. She couldn't remember what she used to think, it seemed like a thousand years ago. Now abortion was no longer something she just had an opinion about, but was an ugly word that filled her with panic. She had to tell someone quickly! But she couldn't!

The right thing to do would be to tell her Mum, or the school nurse or maybe her best friend Jasmine. Any fourteen-year-old who became pregnant should talk to her Mum or the school nurse or preferably both. That was the right thing to do. Everyone knew that. But the right thing didn't feel like a good thing when it applied to her.

What would her Mum say?

At first she would look worried. Emily could put up with that. Then she would say that Emily was too young to be having sex and start talking about contraception in the future and having an abortion now. She would be so annoyingly practical, just as Emily herself would have been towards Jasmine, if it had been her that was pregnant.

She would feel really embarrassed if she talked to the school nurse, but maybe she could do it. Perhaps all she would need to do would be to take a pill when it was this early. The nurse would know. In that case Mum and Dad would never need to know anything about it.

Well, they could know. She was their child after all. But not Steve, he mustn't ever know! Neither should Jasmine really!

Everything would be fine. So why was she in such a panic? Maybe because her stupid body didn't understand anything, it was too busy trying to change itself into a mother!

13

Abortion

Questions for Emily's story

1 Emily feels it's not right to talk about abortion as if it were simply a maths problem with a right or wrong answer. What do you think?

2 Why shouldn't Stephen, Emily's boyfriend know that she's pregnant?

3 Emily thinks that if you're only fourteen and still at school then abortion is the only solution. What do you think?

4 Should boys be more involved in discussions about what a pregnant woman should do?

5 Why doesn't Emily want to talk to an outsider, like her friend or the nurse, about her situation?

6 Would it be easier to talk to a family member or someone like a nurse or doctor?

7 Is Emily too young to have sex?

8 What do you think she should do?

2 Abortion

Jasmine's Story

The class was discussing abortion, but Jasmine was having difficulty concentrating. All she wanted to do was to stand up and shout at them.

"No!" she wanted to shout. "You haven't got the right to sit there and discuss whether I have the right to live or not. I'm here, and I intend to stay here. It's not an 'ethical problem' it's a fact!"

But she didn't say anything, instead she contented herself with sitting quietly and looking thoughtful. She was angry with her mother.

First, she was angry that her mother could have even considered having an abortion when she was pregnant with Jasmine. And secondly that she had to keep telling Jasmine about it over and over again.

There are some things parents should just keep quiet about, and that your mother considered having an abortion when she was pregnant with you was certainly one of them! That's the sort of thing you shouldn't ever have to hear.

Jasmine had heard the story loads of times and it always had the same tearful ending.

"But now I'm so happy that I didn't go ahead. You are the most wonderful thing I have. I don't know what I'd do without you Jasmine!"

First, she would tell the story of how she had fallen in love with Jasmine's father even though he was married.

"But he and his wife weren't at all happy, and he said they were definitely going to get a divorce. But he never did." (Surely she could have worked that one out for herself, the stupid woman. You can pick that up from any problem page!)

She always continued with the story of how lonely and confused she felt when she realised she was pregnant, and her boyfriend just didn't want to know. Then how she'd gone to a clinic to see about an abortion.

"You must understand love, I was so young and didn't have a permanent job, and I just couldn't see how I could cope with a child on my own."

It had been too late for an abortion and they'd been really unkind to her at the clinic. Mum had cried all the way home. She'd even thought about jumping off the nearest bridge. (Sometimes cutting her wrists in the bath was a variation.)

"Write it down and send it to a magazine!" Jasmine wanted to shout at her. "Then I won't have to hear it again and you can get paid for it too!"

She didn't say it though, because she didn't want to upset her Mum, so she just sat there and listened to it all and tried to distance herself from 'the happy ending' and all the hugs and cries of how glad her mother was now that she hadn't had an abortion.

Yes, but surely Jasmine was happy that her Mum hadn't had an abortion?

Weeell, not happy, that was the wrong word, more like angry. Now she was alive it was her right to exist, until she died of old age, or whatever she was going to die of. No-one could get rid of her now she was here and alive.

Maybe it wasn't always a lot of fun being Jasmine, but that was another matter. No matter how bad she sometimes felt, every cell in her body wanted to live. Her Mum of all people shouldn't debate whether or not she had the right to live. It was sick.

"This is an important ethical problem, it doesn't have a clear answer and is one that everyone must find their own solution to," summed up the teacher.

Perhaps Jasmine could have agreed with the teacher if it hadn't been so personal for her. Everything is different when it applies to you.

For a while she thought about saying so, but the discussion was nearly over so she just swallowed her feelings and ran out of the classroom at break time.

Abortion

Questions for Jasmine's story

1 Should abortion be discussed simply as a question of ethics? Jasmine doesn't think so.

2 What would you say to Jasmine if she told you her story?

3 Should a child ever be told that their mother had considered having an abortion?

4 Should something that important be kept a secret? Can secrets sometimes be a good thing?

5 Why do you think Jasmine's mother feels the need to keep telling her about an abortion that never happened?

6 Perhaps Jasmine' mother talks too much, but can we understand her even a little? Should Jasmine try to understand her?

7 Do you think it would have been wrong for Jasmine' mother to have had an abortion in her situation?

Abortion

Questions for both stories

1 What might happen if Emily and Jasmine started to talk to each other about abortion?

2 Do you think they'd be able to understand each other's point of view?

3 Can a subject like abortion be discussed without involving people's feelings?

4 What would be the best way to cope with your own strong feelings, and other people's, in such a discussion?

5 Can the subject of abortion be discussed without a balanced presentation of both side's views?

3 Jump! Jump!

Lisa's Story

Lisa had a headache. She was getting headaches almost every day now, and pains in her stomach too. Was it possible to get pains in your body just because you were unhappy? She was annoyed with herself too, why did she miss her old teacher so much? It wasn't the end of the world just because they'd had a supply teacher for so long, after all, their old teacher had to be allowed to take maternity leave. She'd even come into school the week before and brought little Simon with her. That was fun, everything had felt normal again. Otherwise, nothing seemed normal at school these days.

She really missed her teacher, actually anyone who was a real teacher, not like this new man.

She didn't know exactly what a teacher should be like. This one was very nice but that was the only positive thing that could be said about him. They didn't have lessons any more, they just had mayhem and shouting. Her class had never been a difficult one. Maybe they talked a bit too much sometimes, their teacher had sometimes told them off about it, but that was normal. The teacher liked her class and the class like their teacher. It was only when this new one had arrived that things started to go wrong. Maybe not immediately, at first they were just a bit rowdy, but after a week it was a total catastrophe.

Lisa chewed the end of her pen. What had he said? Were they meant to read to themselves or should they be picking out certain words from the passage? She hadn't managed to hear. Not that it made much difference, no-one else was working anyway. Right now they were passing the

teacher's bag round the classroom. Most people took a book or some paper out and threw it on the floor before they passed the bag on. Lisa absentmindedly took out a pen and put it on her desk, then she passed the bag on.

How did it get to be this bad, she wondered? At first they'd tested him. Who was this tall, stooped person in the stained jacket? He looked harmless enough, but was he? And yes, he was. Then everyone had started doing just what they liked. Talking to their friends, reading magazines or even walking out of the classroom. He just didn't seem to care. The class simply took no notice of him, he could have been invisible, and the noise in the classroom couldn't have been worse if they'd had no teacher at all. That was when Lisa started getting headaches.

Soon that was no longer enough. Some of the boys, Mike was the worst, decided that it would be great fun to torment him. That's when Lisa started getting pains in her stomach.

The poor supply teacher had a hunted look about him and Mike and his gang kept going after him. It got worse and worse and more and more of the class joined in, even the girls. Even if he was pathetic, as everyone said he was, he still had the right to be left alone. It was pure bullying. They should leave him alone, it wasn't right. Lisa wanted to cry. Today it was worse than ever. She wanted to do something but all she could do was sit quietly.

"Please God, let this stop," she whispered, looking down at her desk.

Suddenly, the teacher opened the window and climbed onto the windowsill.

"I'll jump, if you don't shut up!" he shouted. "I'll jump!"

Immediately there was a deathly silence. Everyone stared at the teacher who stared back at them all. The classroom was on the fourth floor and he looked completely mad.

Suddenly the blackboard rubber hit him in the face. Mike started chanting and more and more people joined in, until the whole classroom was vibrating like a football stadium.

Lisa's stomach was churning. She was horrified to realise that she too, was shouting along with everyone else: "Jump! Jump! Jump!"

But he didn't jump.

The headmaster heard the racket and came storming in. The class never saw the teacher again, but for several months afterwards Lisa got pains in her stomach every time she thought of him.

Jump! Jump!

Questions for Lisa's story

1 Can headaches and stomach pains be caused by just being unhappy?

2 Is the man an incompetent teacher?

3 Why does the class behave so badly with this teacher?

4 Why did Lisa take a pen out of the teacher's bag?

5 Could Lisa have done something else instead of sitting quietly and watching?

6 How could she join in and shout "Jump!" with the others?

3 Jump! Jump!

Mike's Story

In the middle of the term Mike's class got a supply teacher. He didn't seem quite normal, Mike saw that immediately, and the man would be with them for almost a year as their teacher had just had a baby and was on maternity leave. Typical! She could have thought of her class instead of just thinking of having babies. Well, he shouldn't complain, this could be really cool.

Mike hadn't really settled in before his teacher went on maternity leave. He'd been a bit of a loner as the other cowards in the class kept out of his way, and he had just been biding his time. Now was his chance.

This tall, gangly loser with the stooped back and dirty glasses was his chance. He wore a jacket with stains on it and baggy combat trousers just like Mike's. Who did he think he was? He probably thought he looked cool but now it was Mike's chance to take over, to show them who was King!

Mike started slowly.

"Your glasses are all filthy," he said in a friendly voice. "I'll clean them for you."

The supply teacher laughed uncertainly.

"Thanks," he said. "That's good of you, but I can manage."

Mike snatched off his glasses, spat on them and rubbed them with his jumper. The kids sitting closest to him started giggling and Mike handed the glasses back with an exaggerated bow.

"There you are Sir!"

He got lots of laughs. ("Yes! This works!" he thought.)

The teacher took his glasses.

"Thanks," he said, nervously.

More laughs.

It was like a bullfight. Mike was thoroughly enjoying himself. It could be a dangerous game if he made a mistake but he didn't plan on making any mistakes.

"Nice trousers!" he said, and pulled gently at the back of the teacher's baggy trousers.

"Yes, it's good to be fashionable," grinned the man.

Now he had created an opening, it was time to attack.

"There's room in your trousers if you have an accident!" shouted Mike.

The class roared with laughter and the teacher said nothing.

Mike was in his element. He had become King, it had been as easy as that.

All he had to do was keep the show going. Mike christened the supply teacher 'The Dweeb'. And every day Mike and his court found new jokes to play on him. It was great fun. Mike was having such a good time that he had pains in his stomach. If the teacher tried to write on the board, he was pelted with erasers and as soon as he turned his back his bag disappeared and was passed round the class and all his things were spread between the desks.

Still he smiled nervously at the class, and acted as if nothing was happening. Mike was forced to find even worse things to do. If he stopped then he wouldn't be King anymore. Everyone wanted new entertainment and he didn't intend to disappoint his public. Everyday there was more mischief and every time was just a little worse than the last.

Then what happened? The stupid teacher opened the window and stood on the windowsill. They were four floors up.

"I'll jump!" he screamed. "I'll jump if you don't shut up."

He was staring like a lunatic at Mike. The class was deathly silent. All eyes were on Mike and the supply teacher. The moment of truth, thought Mike. Just before the matador kills the bull, that's when the matador and the bull become one.

So why did he suddenly feel so sick? And why was he thinking "Oh God, please stop this, I can't." Then he grabbed the blackboard rubber, aimed and threw it. It hit the teacher right in the mouth, and then Mike started chanting.

He started off chanting really quietly, then he got louder and louder and more and more of the class joined in.

27

His stomach felt like it was going to burst with pain, but Mike felt wild with excitement at the same time. He really was the King. His loyal people hadn't disappointed him. It was wonderful when he and the rest of the class joined together with one will and one voice. The class almost raised the roof, shouting:

"Jump! Jump! Jump!"

The headmaster rushed into the room. Immediately, everyone became quiet and still. The teacher climbed down from the windowsill and disappeared through the door. They never saw him again.

Mike crept off to the toilets and was sick. Then he cried. He sobbed and sobbed like a baby.

He couldn't understand what he was feeling. Thank goodness no-one came in and saw him.

Jump! Jump!

Questions for Mike's story

1 Why is Mike so rude about his teacher who is on maternity leave?

2 What does he gain from bullying the supply teacher?

3 Why does he think of the bullying as 'bullfighting' and 'entertainment'?

4 Mike seems to feel that the class forced him to lead the bullying. Is this the case?

5 Why does Mike have stomach ache?

6 Does Mike want to be stopped? If so, why doesn't he just stop himself?

7 Mike doesn't know why he is crying and being sick. What do you think?

Jump! Jump!

Questions for both stories

1 Bullying often needs a mob and a mob needs a leader, most people just follow. Do we change our behaviour when we become part of a crowd?

2 If so, is there anything we can do about it?

3 Can it sometimes feel good to be part of a crowd? Is that necessarily a bad thing?

4 Do bullies always need the support of a crowd? Do they ever act alone?

5 It wasn't just the supply teacher who suffered badly during his time with the class, everyone else did too. In what way?

6 Is any one person more responsible for what happened in the classroom than the others? If so, who is it?

7 The class needs time to recover and to become the group it was before the new teacher started. Everyone involved is responsible for this recovery, but who is most responsible?

Continued …

8 The supply teacher's feelings aren't described here but they are probably the easiest to imagine. How do you think he felt? Will it ever be possible for him to become a good teacher?

9 How will Mike fit into a class that has had time to recover? Can he fit in?

10 If Mike was no longer in the class could it be described as being different or having recovered?

4   Pennies from Heaven?

Caroline's story

Wow, the woman was so beautiful!

It's not true that it is just boys who look at girls. Girls do it just as much, and then compare themselves to what they see. Caroline couldn't stop watching the young woman who'd just stopped to take out money from the cash point. She was beautiful. She had a perfect figure and was wearing an expensive looking top and an elegant skirt cut well above the knee. With legs like hers you could get away with a skirt like that. Caroline made a face, she always tried to hide her dumpy legs as much as she could. Life is so unfair. Of course, this was no girl she was looking at, the woman was quite old, she must be almost thirty.

Whenever Caroline complained about her figure her Dad would tell her the story of 'The Ugly Duckling'.

"You're fine just as you are, Caroline," he'd say. "There are lots of things going on in your body at your age. I've read about film stars and super models who thought they were really ugly when they were thirteen. Then they grew into themselves."

She snorted.

That was just to make her feel better. It was this Friday that she'd been invited to Mel's house, not in a few years time when she'd – maybe – grown into herself. John was sure to be there, and she had absolutely nothing to

wear. She looked dreadful in her horrible old clothes. Couldn't a good fairy magic her some cash? Even if it wouldn't change her shape at least she'd feel a bit more confident if she had something nice to wear.

Maybe she should make a wish, or say a prayer!

"Dear God, can you please fix it so that I get some cash for clothes and then make John notice me on Friday. Please!" She laughed to herself.

The woman at the cash point looked miserable. Beautiful but miserable. She didn't look much fun, just grumpy and stressed. She fumbled with her bank card, dropped it, picked it up again and then put it into the machine. She looked impatiently at her watch, keyed in her PIN and then snatched back the card, threw it into her bag and rushed off.

Anyone who could just stick a card into a machine and get money from it couldn't have too much to worry about. Caroline's pocket money had to cover everything. She couldn't get money from a hole in the wall.

Caroline felt bitter. She didn't think a fairy or even God would give her any cash, or John either, come to that.

Some people have everything she thought. Beauty, money, everything and they still look miserable. Caroline walked passed the cash point. There was no-one there now. But what did she see? There was money in the machine and a receipt at the top. The woman had obviously been so rushed that she'd forgotten to take her money. Caroline didn't stop to think. Her left hand seemed to take on a life of its own. It shot out and took the five wonderful £20 notes and stuffed them into her coat pocket in one movement. She didn't stop, didn't look at the cash point, just kept on going down the street at the same pace as before. This was just unbelievable!

"Wow! Someone was listening after all," she thought.

The woman came running back towards the cash point. For a moment Caroline considered calling out and saying with a smile: "You forgot your money!" and giving her the £20 notes.

She really did, for one moment she thought about doing it.

But the moment passed and instead she kept on walking. She didn't run and she didn't look around, but even though nothing happened she felt that she was being followed right up to her front door.

How lucky can you get? She hadn't stolen the money, it was more like finding it in the street. Well, actually she had found it in the street, hadn't she? She tried to think about what she'd buy with the money when she got the chance, but it was quite difficult to feel really happy.

That was at first, but a bit later when she went shopping she felt really happy. She'd almost forgotten the woman at the cash point. She must be rich. One hundred pounds wouldn't mean a thing to her, you could tell that by the way she was dressed.

"Thank you, whoever is looking out for me!" said Caroline, a little hesitantly. "I really needed this money more than she did and you understood that didn't you? And you won't forget the thing with John either will you?"

Pennies from Heaven?

Questions for Caroline's story

1 Should Caroline have given the money back to the woman?

2 How many people do you think would have done so? Would you?

3 Why did Caroline find it difficult to feel happy at first?

4 What had changed by the time she went shopping?

5 What made her think the woman didn't really need the money?

6 Caroline decides that someone must have listened to her and realised that she needed the money more than the woman at the cash point. Why does she come to this conclusion?

4 Pennies from Heaven?

Monica's story

How on earth could someone be called 'Sylvester'? What a strange name!

"I'm sure I came into being after a New Year's Eve dinner!" he'd laughed when she asked him about it. "My parents are German and in Germany New Year's Eve is called St Sylvester's Day. That's why I love lobster and champagne!"

"And, of course, you never eat anything else," she'd teased.

"Oh never. When I've got the money that is, but I don't always have the money," he'd said trying to look tragic. "So I'm not a very good catch in that respect."

"Nor am I," she said. It just slipped out before she could stop it.

She blushed and kept quiet. She didn't want to seem too keen, as they'd been enjoying each other's company and flirting a little.

"It's obvious really, because I was born on the 10th of October," he'd said.

"What do you mean, obvious?"

She hadn't really been listening because she'd been too busy wondering if she'd made a fool of herself by seeming too interested in him.

"Well, between Sylvester Night and the 10th of October is nine months and ten days, so that fits in well with my theory."

"Then you were born ten days late."

"I always turn up at the last minute," he'd said laughing.

"Me too," she'd laughed.

(It was on the tip of her tongue to say, "We wouldn't have very punctual children, would we?" But luckily she stopped herself just in time.)

Had that really been only a week ago? She felt as if she'd known him forever, but they'd only met three times. They'd gone to the cinema and then out for a burger afterwards, they didn't have enough money for anything else. Today was the 10th of October and she'd plucked up courage to ask him to dinner for a birthday treat.

"And of course we'll have lobster and champagne," she'd said as a joke. She'd been terrified that he might have already arranged something else.

Instead he'd seemed really pleased. Of course he'd come!

Monica felt that if there was going to be any future for her and Sylvester it would be obvious tonight.

"A lobster dinner might be dangerous," she laughed to herself. Then she decided she would really do it.

She couldn't really afford to, not after she'd bought the new outfit to wear when they had been to the cinema on Saturday. She'd blown the last of

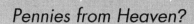

her wages, but at least she got free meals at work, and she did love the new clothes. Monica was relying on her sister to lend her some money and she had agreed to transfer the £100 that she kept for emergencies into Monica's account. It would be a loan until her next pay day.

She had to hurry.

She needed to get the money from the cash point and then do the shopping. Champagne and some wine, French bread, butter, lettuce, tomatoes, mayonnaise and what else? Lobster, of course, but she'd go to a proper fishmonger for that. What time did they close?

Rushing, rushing! First she had to find a cash machine.

Yes, there was one.

It was twenty to five. She needed to go to the fishmonger first, before it shut. Wasn't there one near the supermarket? She thought there was. Hopefully the queues wouldn't be too long.

She dropped her cash card, bent down to pick it up, pushed it into the machine, punched in her PIN, took out the card and threw it into her bag. Then she rushed off in the direction of the supermarket.

The money! She'd forgotten the money!

She ran back to the cash machine. There was no-one there, but there was no money either, only a lonely receipt fluttering in the breeze.

Someone had taken the money.

She'd only turned her back for a couple of minutes but apparently that was enough, in that time someone had taken her money. It was all she had!

In about two hours Sylvester would be arriving at her house. What was she going to do? Serve him cornflakes? She didn't even have any milk!

She stood staring at the cash machine for a long time. She read the receipt over and over again as if it might give her a clue.

"I hate living in this place," she thought. "It's full of crooks and thieves! Whoever took the money must have seen me, I can't have been gone for more than ten seconds, if that. How could someone do that? It's so mean and heartless."

She quickly made her way home. She kept her head down, trying not to look at the people she passed and hoping that they wouldn't notice that she was crying.

Pennies from Heaven?

Questions for Monica's story

1 Monica was right to think that whoever had taken the money must have seen her. What kind of person would you have to be to do a thing like that?

2 Do you think Monica was just unlucky? Would most people have called her back and given her the money? What would you have done?

3 What do you think she will do now for the evening?

4 Is she right to worry about what Sylvester will think?

5 Should Monica have borrowed from her sister when she had already spent all of her own money?

41

Pennies from Heaven?

Questions for both stories

1 Do you think Monica would have felt as bitter towards crooks and thieves in the town if she'd known what Caroline was thinking?

2 Do you think Caroline would have kept the money if she'd known what Monica wanted it for?

3 Caroline isn't immoral. What makes her take the money despite her feelings?

4 Did Caroline need the money more than Monica? Why does Caroline think she does?

5 Is there any excuse for what Caroline did?

6 Is there much difference between Monica borrowing money she could not really afford and Caroline taking money that's not hers?

5 The First Date

Chris's Story

They had decided the day before yesterday, at the school disco.

He had danced quite a bit (well, twice anyway) with Katie who was in his class but mainly they just sat together and chatted while they ate their crisps. She was really nice. She didn't say much, but neither did he and she was pretty, really pretty.

She knew about computer games too, probably because she had a brother. It's always good when a girl has a brother, thought Chris, it makes her a bit more human somehow.

Just as the last song was playing and he thought that he'd made it through the evening, she had touched his hand.

"Hey, Chris …," she'd said, and then stopped.

"What?" he'd replied, without much enthusiasm.

"Oh … nothing," she'd said and looked down at the table.

"Tell me anyway."

"Well, Tash has been on a date with Ricky, and Anna has with Ben and Mel with Felix …"

"I know, they must be mad."

"So, I was wondering if … I mean, everyone has been on a date with someone. What do you think? Or maybe it's a stupid idea…"

Chris suddenly felt really hot inside, as if he'd drunk some tea too quickly. This was his chance. Even though he was terrified, he still wanted to say yes. He realised that the thing he wanted most in life, right at that moment, was a date with Katie.

"We can do that," he said in his coolest voice. "I'll pick you up on Friday at around six o'clock, will that be OK? Then we can decide what we want to do."

Katie had nodded eagerly and smiled happily.

Friday arrived, and Chris was on his way to meet Katie.

Was he regretting it?

Not a bit! For the last few days he hadn't been able to think of anything other than his date with Katie. Just before he went to sleep at night, he imagined the two of them together on their date. Then he would jump as if he'd had an electric shock. What would he say? What should he do? Should he ring and say he was ill? No, he couldn't do that, he was madly in love with Katie and he was going to meet her on Friday even if it killed him. It was strange how quickly you could fall in love, it was as if she'd pressed a button when she asked about the date.

He rang the door bell.

Katie opened the door, all ready to go.

Oh no, what was she wearing? Chris was just wearing his jeans and a (not very clean) t-shirt. Katie was all dressed up and there was no escaping the fact that she was stunningly pretty.

They walked towards the town centre without saying a word.

"Shall we go to the pictures?" suggested Chris.

"Yes," she'd like that. "What about that new comedy?"

"It is only rated 12A," said Chris sarcastically. "How about 'Army of Fear' instead?"

"You have to be over fifteen for that," said Katie, hesitantly. "We're only thirteen."

"They won't say anything," said Chris, hoping it was true. "I've got in before and anyway you could pass for a twenty-year-old now you're all dressed up."

"Thanks," said Katie and smiled.

So they went to see 'Army of Fear'.

It was a bit scary in the cinema, but mainly because Chris was wondering whether or not he should hold Katie's hand. He was trying to pluck up the courage when suddenly she took his hand. It got a bit sweaty after a while, but he didn't dare take his hand away. She seemed so confident.

Afterwards they went for a burger. They didn't say much. They talked about the film a bit, about how it had been good, well, quite good or at least not too bad. Then it was time to take her home.

Should you kiss a girl when you take her home after a first date, he wondered? It felt really embarrassing, but at the same time he wanted to do it. As they stood at the front door he plucked up his courage, and threw himself forwards and planted a kiss on the side of Katie's mouth.

"Bye, see you," he shouted, and ran off.

"Bye, see you," she called back. "And thanks for tonight."

"You're welcome," called Chris and then was cross with himself for not thinking of something wittier.

She must think I'm a right loser, he thought.

The First Date

Questions for Chris's Story

1 Do people really fall in love so quickly? What made Chris think he had fallen in love?

2 Why did Chris say at first that people who went on dates were mad, then agree to one himself?

3 Why does Chris feel so nervous and think about cancelling the date?

4 Was the choice of film a good one? Was Chris right to insist on the horror film?

5 Did Chris feel the date was successful? What about Katie?

6 Why did Chris end the date feeling like he was a loser?

47

5 The First Date

Katie's Story

She had been watching Chris for a while, but of course he hadn't noticed.

Then they went to the disco…

He had danced with her and then they'd sat and chatted, but she'd said some really stupid things. He was so cool, and really nice and he was good looking too.

Then she'd asked him if he wanted to go on a date with her! She didn't know how she'd managed to pluck up the courage, but when he hadn't said anything she just had to do it. She couldn't believe it when he actually said yes!

A few of her friends had started going on dates, but no-one had asked her out so far. Now she felt pleased about it, because she wanted her first date to be with Chris. I suppose a date is a way of trying things out, to see if you want to be together, she thought. Then again, if you've been on a date with someone you're practically a couple anyway, unless it is a complete disaster.

What if it was a complete disaster? What if she couldn't think of anything to say or if she said something really stupid and he thought she was a hopeless case? He would be on his way to meet her by now, so it was too late to back out. She'd been ready for at least an hour, even though she'd

changed her outfit about a hundred times. She didn't want to look like she was trying to seem too old, but didn't want to look too young either. It would be awful if he thought she looked like a kid.

He rang the doorbell. Straight away she regretted getting dressed up, but it was too late now. He'd just come in his normal clothes, that's how confident he was. They agreed to go to see a film. She wanted to go and see a comedy she'd heard was really good and a bit romantic, but they decided on 'Army of Fear', a horror film. She didn't find it too scary in the end though. Maybe it was because she wasn't really concentrating. Waiting to see if Chris would hold her hand was more scary than anything else!

He didn't though, so she plucked up courage and took his hand instead. He didn't seem to be shy but maybe he was, you never know with boys. The most embarrassing thing was that her hand was really sweaty, she wanted to dry it on the seat or something but she didn't dare in case he noticed. They sat holding hands while the actors chopped off each other's arms and legs and screamed a lot. (She still thought the comedy would have been a much better choice, but maybe Chris wouldn't have agreed.)

Later they went for a burger. She had her own money but he offered to pay for her. That was really nice.

"My treat next time," she said.

He just grunted. Did that mean there wouldn't be a next time, or did it mean he wanted to pay next time too? Or did it just mean he had a mouth full of chips and that was as much as he could manage? She couldn't tell.

They talked a bit about the film while they ate. They decided it was OK, but they'd seen better, and worse too, of course.

Then it was time to go home.

This was the critical moment.

Would he kiss her? Wasn't that how it should happen, he should kiss her when he dropped her off, unless the date had been a complete failure? Had it been a failure? She didn't really know.

He seemed so cool but what if he was really shy? What if he wanted to kiss her but didn't dare to? Should she kiss him? No, she couldn't do that, but why not? She'd read in a magazine that men didn't like pushy women, but who cared about women's magazines?

Oh, please let him kiss her so that she didn't have to kiss him, because she didn't think she would dare! She'd never kissed anyone before, even though she was nearly fourteen. Was that a world record?

Oh no, he wasn't going to do it … He was getting ready to leave.

Suddenly, he threw himself forward and kissed her, not quite full on the lips but on the side of her mouth, then he ran off.

"Bye, see you," he shouted.

He had kissed her, he loved her, she was ecstatic!

"Bye, see you," she shouted. "And thanks for tonight."

"You're welcome," said Chris in his usual cool way.

Katie was singing inside. He loves me! He kissed me!

Mind you, he didn't quite reach my mouth. Maybe I just moved my head at the wrong moment. I just hope he doesn't think I'm an idiot.

The First Date

Questions for Katie's Story

1 Why was Katie so nervous?

2 What does Katie think of Chris? How does she think he feels?

3 Why was is so important for her to wear the right clothes?

4 Is it really a world record not to have been kissed when you're almost fourteen?

5 Did Katie think the date was a success?

6 What might Chris think?

The First Date

Questions for both stories

1 Do you fall in love with someone because you like things about them, or do you appreciate them more because you're in love with them?

2 What makes us fall in love with someone? And why does it often not last?

3 Who was the most nervous about the date? Who was the most confident?

4 Both Chris and Katie have thoughts and ideas about what a date should be like. What are their ideas?

5 Are their ideas a help or a hindrance?

6 Both Chris and Katie are worried about what the other will think of them, even though they aren't critical themselves. Why is this? Does this happen in other friendships?

7 Would it have been better if they had discussed what they were going to do on their date before they met?

Continued …

8 Who had sweaty hands, and why?

9 Is it embarrassing to kiss someone?

10 Do you think there's a big difference between the way boys and girls think and feel?

6 Girl Talk/Boy Talk

Chris's story

It was lunchtime. A group of boys were hanging around, waiting for the bell for the next lesson.

"I heard that you'd had a date with Katie on Friday," said Ben to Chris. "What did you do?"

"We saw 'Army of Fear' and then we went for a burger," said Chris.

"How was it?" asked Ben, curiously.

"Not bad, I've seen better films, but it was OK, and you know what burgers are like."

Ben was getting impatient.

"Stop messing around, you know exactly what I mean. Come on, tell us, she looks dead sexy. What's she really like?"

"She's great," said Chris a bit hesitantly. "She's fine."

"Come on," said Ben. "Did you kiss or anything?"

"What do you think? Of course we kissed. To tell the truth I didn't see much of the film."

"You're kidding," said Ben sounding both impressed and disbelieving. "It was the same when Anna and I went out on a date." He grinned. "It was lucky it was dark, well, you know…"

"Other people couldn't see what you were up to," explained Nick, just to be sure that they all understood.

"Oh yes, she'd die if she thought people were watching," said Chris grinning.

"Have you kissed many girls? I was just wondering …" asked Ben.

"I've never counted," Chris said lightly. "Not many," he added modestly. (That wasn't quite true, as Katie was the first girl he had ever kissed, but he wasn't going to tell Ben that! One girl isn't 'many'. In his own way Chris was very truthful.)

"She's great looking, isn't she?" said Nick.

"Yes she's attractive, really attractive," said Chris.

"So, does she wear a bra?" pressed Nick. "Did you get a chance to find out?"

"No comment," he said feeling a bit out of his depth. "Things like that are private."

The boys were impressed. It almost sounded as if he had had a chance to find out.

"What else did you do?" Felix asked. "You can tell us, you know we won't tell anyone."

"No," said the other boys getting excited, "we won't say anything."

Chris thought about repeating "No comment," but it would never work a second time and even if it did then Katie would get a bad reputation and that would be terrible. He was in love with Katie and he suddenly remembered it, he was really in love with Katie.

"No, no, no," he said instead. "Chill out, what do you think she is – it was only our first date."

"Oh well, never mind, I expect you'll get further next time," said Felix.

"She didn't say anything about that," said Chris sharply, "and anyway we're going out together now."

The boys started to apologise.

"Oh, you're going out together, well that's different."

"Of course you don't want to give details about someone you're going out with."

"You should have said."

"I did say," said Chris, "I told you just now."

"Yes, but straight away."

"Well, I'm not sure I realised we were going out together until just now," thought Chris to himself, but he didn't say it out loud.

So – he was going out with Katie. Now all he had to do was tell her that! What if she got angry and said no? He'd be so embarrassed. He was really nervous until at last he caught sight of her at the end of a corridor surrounded by other girls. He took a deep breath and pushed his way through the group and asked her in a whisper if she would go out with him.

"I already am," she whispered back to him. "I've already told everyone."

"So have I," said Chris. "So that's all settled then."

Girl Talk/Boy Talk

Questions for Chris's story

1 Chris can't resist exaggerating a bit when he talks about the date. Do most people do that?

2 What impression does he give of himself? What impression does he give of Katie?

3 Why won't he talk about Katie and what he had or hadn't done with her on their date?

4 Would he have been more explicit about what they had done if he hadn't been in love with Katie? Would it have made any difference if what he was saying had been true?

5 Why does he say he's going out with her?

6 Do boys really talk like this when they're together or is it just something adults think they do?

6 Girl Talk/Boy Talk

Katie's story

The girls were jumping with curiosity.

"How was it Katie?"
"What did you do?"
"Is he as cute as he seems?"
"Are you going to see him again?"
"Did he kiss you?"

Katie laughed happily and then she started to tell.

"I could tell almost straight away that he was in love with me and I'm in love with him too. He's really sweet, but at the same time he's quite shy so I had to help him along. But I had to be careful so I didn't scare him off."

The girls nodded knowingly.

"You have to get the right balance," said Anna. "When I went out with Ben he was so shy I couldn't believe it, but of course I pretended I hadn't noticed."

Yes, they all agreed, that would ruin everything straight away.

"What did you do?"

"First we went to see a film."

"What did you see?"

"I don't really remember, it was a horror film, but all I could think about was whether or not he was going to hold my hand."

"Did he?"

"He was afraid to, so I held his instead. He seemed really happy when I did. I had to search for ages in the dark though, before I found his hand."

"Are you sure that's what you were doing?" asked Tash giggling.

"Whatever do you mean?" asked Katie laughing, although she understood what Tash meant.

All the girls exploded with laughter.

"Oh no!" said Katie. "He would have died if we had done much more than hold hands!"

"So," wondered Mel. "You didn't you sit and kiss all through the film?"

"Not so much then, no." Katie exaggerated a bit.

"We did much more later by my front door when he took me home – he got quite wild. He just threw himself at me and wouldn't stop kissing me."

"That must have been awful," said Mel.

"Not really, it was quite nice. He was really gentle but at the same time really wild. But it wasn't awful," said Katie.

"So he didn't try to do anything else?"

"We were standing at my front door and anyway he's not like that. He loves me, at least I think he does."

"Did he say so?"

"Not quite, but almost and you can tell that sort of thing."

The girls nodded in agreement.

"Oh yes, you can always tell."
"Didn't he touch you at all?"
"Did he want to do anything else?"

Katie realised she needed to put a stop to this.

"Of course he wanted to," she said. "But boys can't have everything at once, or they just think you're a whore and don't respect you."

The girls nodded.

"Boys are so difficult."
"But cute too!"
"Will you have sex with him if he wants you to?"

Katie pretended to think about it.

"I don't know, maybe sometime, but it would have to be when we've been going out for a long time."

"So you're really going out? Seriously?"

The girls sounded very impressed.

"Of course we are," said Katie. "He wouldn't take no for an answer."

At that moment Chris came over.

He'd been looking for her, and her heart was in her mouth. What if he said in front of everyone that they weren't going out – she didn't know what she would do.

"Katie," whispered Chris. "Will you go out with me?"

"I already am," she whispered back. "I've told everyone already."

"Me too," said Chris. "So that's settled then."

Girl Talk/Boy Talk

Questions for Katie's story

1 Katie can't resist exaggerating a bit when she tells her friends about her date. Is that usual?

2 What impression does she give of herself? What impression does she give of Chris?

3 Is this how girls usually talk about boys and dates?

4 Although she wants to sound experienced Katie is afraid of getting a bad reputation. Are girls often afraid of what people will think?

5 How much should a girl tell her friends about what happened on a date? How much can they exaggerate?

6 Why does Katie say that she and Chris are going out together?

Girl Talk/Boy Talk

Questions for both stories

1 Both Katie and Chris exaggerate when they tell their stories. Who do you think exaggerates most? Who sticks most closely to what actually happened?

2 Who is keener to tell their friends about the date? Why is this?

3 Are there specific differences between how boys and girls talk to each other? Are these stories realistic?

4 People want to talk to friends about things that are important to them, but there is always a risk of betraying someone you like by talking too much. If you were Katie would you be upset by some of the things Chris was saying? What if you were Chris?

5 It has always been the case that a boy who has lots of girlfriends is thought of very differently from a girl who has lots of boyfriends. Does this double standard still exist? If so, can we do anything about it?

6 What is the best way of setting boundaries for what happens between a couple on a date?

Continued …

7 In these stories Chris and Katie are both new to dating, but they want people to think they are more experienced than they really are. How much do you think this happens in real life?

8 Is it always possible to tell when people are boasting about their experiences?

9 Have you ever felt that you might have to go further than you want to with someone just because it seems everyone else is?

10 Would Chris and Katie have decided they were going out together if it hadn't been for their talks with their friends?

7 Who Needs a Watch?

Lee's story

Lee had been given a watch for his thirteenth birthday.

He got other presents too and had a great day, but the watch was left on his desk.

Lee didn't like watches. Watches were evil gadgets that stopped you finishing what you were doing and Lee hated being forced to stop things when he was enjoying them. Like stopping his computer game because it was time to go to bed, or turning off the light because it was time to go to sleep, even though he was at an exciting part in his book, or worst of all waking up in the morning when the alarm went off even though his body was telling him it wanted to sleep all day.

Watches were evil dictators that controlled people, or at least they did where he came from. Apparently things were better in other countries. In some places people had a more relaxed approach to time keeping, or that's what he'd heard.

Lee had nothing against school except that it started too early in the day. Why couldn't it start at ten or eleven and then go on through the day until you felt you'd had enough? But of course it didn't work like that because clocks wouldn't let it. He liked his teacher but unfortunately the clock ruled her too. Nearly every day when Lee arrived in the classroom she would look at her watch and say in an annoyed voice that actually the lesson had already started and Lee was late.

"No, I'm not," he wanted to say. "You are early. What's the hurry, we've got plenty of time to do what we need to, it's not like it's difficult." He never did though, he was always too polite.

Mum and Dad were nice too, but they were slaves to the time as well and they had something even worse, they had smartphones with diaries. Is nobody free, wondered Lee. At least I want to be.

Now school had finally ended for the day and all he had to do was enjoy himself in his own time. He'd arranged to go home and collect his Warhammer figures and then go straight to his friend Dan's house. They were planning a big field battle. It could take hours, but it was Friday so there was no school the next day. He hadn't had much lunch, so when he got home he ate a couple of sandwiches and read for a bit. Then he got his figures and put them in their special case which had little compartments to protect them. While he was putting them in the case he realised that a couple of the figures he'd painted last night before weren't quite dry, so he quickly got the hairdryer and gave them a blast of warm air to dry them off.

While he was doing it a programme came on the television that he liked, even though it was meant for younger children, but they all had really stupid voices and he could mimic them really well. He watched some of the programme and then Dad called out that dinner was ready. Well, why not, he thought, he had to eat and he was beginning to feel quite hungry again. After dinner he read a bit more. Then he took his Warhammer case and went straight to Dan's.

Strange, it was getting quite dark, even though it was the middle of June. When Dan opened the door he looked furious.

"Oh, it's you," he said angrily. "Did you forget we were going to play Warhammer?"

"No," said Lee, trying to sound enthusiastic and waving his case. "I've got everything with me." He was beginning to realise that something was wrong.

"Well, you can't come in now. Do you know what the time is?" hissed Dan.

"No, you know I don't have a watch."

"It's well after half-past nine and I'm going to bed now."

Lee tried not to show his disappointment.

"Tomorrow then," he said. "Shall we play tomorrow?"

"I'm doing something with my family tomorrow," said Dan. "Bye." Then he slammed the door right in Lee's face.

Who Needs a Watch?

Questions for Lee's story

1 Should people let themselves be ruled by the time?

2 Can we always expect to be able to finish something just because we want to?

3 Do you think Lee would be better at being on time if he wore his watch?

4 Was Dan right to be angry with Lee? After all, Lee turned up that night as they'd arranged.

5 What might Lee think was the reason for Dan being upset with him? Did he realise what the reason was?

7 Who Needs a Watch?

Dan's story

As soon as he got home from school, Dan ate a sandwich as quickly as he could, and then took some juice up to his room.

He'd built a whole battlefield landscape on the table for his Warhammer figures. It had hills, valleys and a lake in the middle with a mountain and a cave. It was the Elves' homeland. Dan and his Dad had been working on it for months, shaping, sculpting and painting, and now it was finished. Today was the big day!

It was great that Lee liked playing Warhammer too. The two boys had spent hours in the Games Workshop learning the rules and spending all their money, and more, on rule books and figures. Then they'd then sat together painting the figures, which was almost the best thing about it all, even though it was really fiddly. Dan hoped that Lee wouldn't arrive until he had his army completely set up – it was going to look brilliant!

Finished! It was looked fantastic. Now Lee could come, it was only just after five o'clock, so they'd have time to play for four or five hours if they wanted to. Dan had High Elves and Lee had Vampire Counts. Lee was going to bring a model church with him to use as barracks for his troops. It could stand at the other end of the lake so that the troops could meet face to face on the lake side.

Dan looked at the clock, it was almost five-thirty. Where was Lee? He'd have to hurry up. He rang Lee's phone to get him to hurry but there was no answer. Dan put the phone down with a sigh.

He fixed some details on the battlefield, but it wasn't much fun any more, he wanted to get on with the battle. Lee had said he was just going home after school to fetch his Warhammer case. What had happened? Dan rang again. Still no answer, so Dan rang the home phone but that was engaged. After a while he tried again but it was still engaged. Some idiot had obviously not put the phone down properly or it was Lee's sister talking to her boyfriend for hours again!

Dan thought about going round to Lee's to get him. A couple of hours ago he might have done, but now he was starting to get angry. Lee could find his own way!

A really stupid programme came on the television which Dan watched, even though it was for babies. Dan lay on his bed and read a magazine to pass the time, but there was still no sign of Lee.

Dinner time came.

"Wasn't Lee going to have dinner with us?" asked Mum, surprised.

"He didn't turn up," muttered Dan.

"But I thought you were going to play Warhammer. Isn't that what you'd arranged?"

"Is he ill?" Dad asked.

"He was fine at school."

"Have you tried to phone him?"

"I've been ringing his mobile all evening, he isn't answering and the home phone is engaged."

Mum looked annoyed.

"It's really inconsiderate of him to let you down like this."

"He can't have really wanted to play" said Dan bitterly, "and he was too much of a coward to tell me. Or maybe he found something more interesting to do with someone else."

Now he was feeling really bad about everything. What made him think that Lee was with someone else and they were having fun together? Dan told himself he was being stupid.

In the end Dan decided he might just as well go to bed. What a boring evening. Suddenly, the doorbell rang. Dan opened it to see Lee standing there with his black Warhammer case. Four hours too late!

"You've decided to turn up now?" asked Dan. "Did you forget or something?"

"No," said Lee happily. "I've got everything with me."

"Do you know what time it is?"

"No, I don't have a watch."

"Well, it's after half-past nine and I'm going to bed!" snapped Dan.

Lee looked disappointed, as if he'd only just realised that it was late.

"Tomorrow then, what about tomorrow?"

Dan snorted.

"I'm doing something with my family", he said. "Bye."

He shut the door.

Who Needs a Watch?

Questions for Dan's story

1 Have you ever waited and waited for someone who didn't turn up? How did you feel?

2 What did Dan think Lee might be doing instead? Why did he start wondering about what Lee was doing?

3 Why did Dan feel so disappointed and angry with Lee?

4 Was Mum right to say that Lee was being inconsiderate towards Dan?

5 Lee turned up in the end, why didn't Dan let him in?

75

Who Needs a Watch?

Questions for both stories

1 Are there times when a watch would be useful?

2 Do people need to be 'slaves to the time'? Is it helpful?

3 Are there countries where people aren't quite so strict about time-keeping?

4 What would it be like if people could start school later and stay until they felt they had done enough?

5 Does time pass just as quickly for someone who is waiting as it does for the person who is late?

6 What was the real reason for Lee being late and what did Dan imagine was the reason?

7 Can people be inconsiderate without meaning to be?

Continued ...

8 Lee didn't mean to be late, 'it just happened'. Is there anything he could have done about it?

9 Lee's teacher thinks he is always late as well, should she do something to help him?

10 Should Dan explain to Lee why he is upset?

77

8 Computer Games

Jason's story

Granddad Samuel had come to stay with them for a week. Jason was pleased, Granddad had been retired for years and years, but he was still really healthy for an old man and was lots of fun. Grandma had been dead for a few years now.

He could be a bit strange at times, but who couldn't? He'd been a vicar somewhere and you could still see signs of that. He would get a sort of tight look around his mouth when someone talked about something he thought was sinful. (And you never knew in advance what Granddad might decide was sinful.) He would mutter things like 'young peple today!' or ask 'Whatever is the world today coming to?'

His grandchildren Jason, Michael and Amy, who was only eight, just thought life was fun and a bit exciting.

"Don't eat biscuits before your dinner, it's sinful", Amy would say, as she took two.

That would make both Granddad and Mum laugh, especially Mum. It was obvious that Mum sometimes got a bit irritated by some of Granddad's ideas about what you should and shouldn't do.

But then she had grown up with him and saw things a bit differently. For example, when Granddad came to visit, Mum would never drink alcohol in front of him, she always had something else instead, even though when he wasn't there she might have a glass of wine. It seems you're never really grown up in your parent's eyes, Jason thought.

He sat down at the computer and started playing his new game. He was concentrating on his reflexes. His score was well ahead of all his friends, but there was always room for improvement. Suddenly he noticed Granddad standing behind him.

"What's that?" he asked. "Where did that come from?"

"You can download it from the internet," said Jason. "But I got it from my friend."

"That building looks like some sort of Cathedral or church. But what are those horrible things on the walls, are they Devil's masks?"

"Yes, they are," said Jason quietly.

Granddad said nothing.

"So what do you have to do in this game then?"

"Frags," said Jason. "You have to get as many frags as possible."

"Yes, but what does 'frags' mean?"

"Look," said Jason. "I'll show you."

A young woman in a tight-fitting outfit came rushing onto the screen with a machine gun in her hand. Jason aimed, and blew her away with a volley of shots. The woman stopped suddenly, fell to the ground and exploded so that limbs and blood spurted in every direction. After a few seconds, what was left of her body sank into the ground and disappeared.

"One frag, one point, because I got her."

"The point of the game is to kill her?" exclaimed Granddad.

"Wait, here come some more. There's another one like her coming back and there are three different enemies over there."

Quickly, figures appeared on the screen from all directions and tried to get the character with the machine gun who was being controlled by Jason.

"You've got to keep moving so you don't get caught," explained Jason as he shot down three women wearing bikinis and three monsters who consisted of nothing but a giant eye and a weapon.

"It's Satanic!" said Granddad, horrified. "And what is that dreadful music?"

"Black Sabbath," said Jason absently. "I added that myself because I thought it was appropriate."

"It certainly is appropriate," said Granddad looking very serious now.

Michael came over to the computer.

"How's it going?" he asked enthusiastically. "Can I have a go now?"

"Wait, I'm just about to complete this level," said Jason. "I've still got eight lives left and if I get four more frags then I've done it."

Granddad looked more serious than the boys had ever seen him look before.

"Turn that Satanic game off!" he said angrily. "It's … it's disgraceful. I need to talk to your mother."

"Have you nearly finished? Can I have a turn now?" pestered Michael.

Jason completed the level and then turned off the computer.

"I think we should leave it until Granddad's gone home again," he said quietly.

Computer Games

Questions for Jason's story

1 Why doesn't Jason's Mum drink alcohol in front of Granddad?

2 Granddad doesn't know anything about computer games, is that why he's so upset or is it because he used to be a Vicar?

3 Could Granddad be right, is the game unsuitable for the boys?

4 Jason has no intention of never playing the game again, but decides to wait until after Granddad goes home. Is he being thoughtful or cowardly?

5 Why do the boys like the game?

6 How might they defend their reasons for playing?

8 Computer Games

Granddad's story

The day before yesterday I arrived to visit my daughter and her family. It's good to see them all. The children have grown up so much since I last saw them. Jason is turning into a pleasant young man who's taller than I am. He's only fourteen but he looks older.

Eleven-year-old Michael is keen on everything related to the military. I don't really like toys that are war-based but I suppose all boys go through these phases. When I was a boy we played war games but it was different then, war was fresher in our minds.

Amy is a happy and healthy eight-year-old, but it seems only yesterday that I baptized her. My wife Mabel was still with me then, before she became ill and died.

I did come here full of good intentions.

Jocelyn and her family are living their lives and I'm coming towards the end of mine. The views of the younger generation aren't always the same as mine, that was something I realised a long time ago. I don't want to be a kill joy. Jocelyn is a good girl and her children are growing up to be fine young people. I think her husband is a good man too, and don't really understand why they decided to separate, but I know that it is none of my business.

Of course, I would have liked it if religion had meant as much to Jocelyn's family as it always has done to me, and did for Mabel too, when she was alive. However, complaining about it won't help, so I say my prayers discreetly and leave it at that. I include them all in my prayers too, they can't stop me from doing that.

That was my intention anyway.

I promised myself on the train that I wouldn't lecture them and try to change their ways, it only has the opposite effect and can make things uncomfortable all round, I know that much.

But today I changed my mind.

Jason was on the computer and was playing some sort of game. I didn't go over to him to moralise, I was interested in what he was doing and he just thought it was fun, I think. Jason was happy to explain the game to me and didn't seem at all put out.

But I was.

If evil exists then that game was surely it!

It was all about killing women, or monsters that seemed to have come from Hell. I'm not exaggerating! The whole idea of the game was to kill as many living things as possible without being killed yourself. It wasn't like Michael's soldiers where he knocks one over when it is supposed to have been killed, Jason shot at the figures on the screen and they were torn into pieces. Arms, legs and heads flew in different directions while the blood squirted onto the screen! This was supposed to be a game and, what's more, Satanic music was playing in the background!

It didn't just remind me of Satanism, it was Satanism! I feel so upset that my beautiful young grandchildren should have their minds and souls poisoned by this sort of thing. I angrily told Jason to turn off the computer, and he did, but I was too upset to be able to explain why.

I must talk to Jocelyn. She is their mother and is responsible for making sure the children aren't damaged. I won't be unfriendly and perhaps it would be better not to mention religion. If she doesn't much believe in God then she's not going to believe in Satan either, but she's a good person and she has sound morals so I'll appeal to them. When she was younger I know she was interested in feminism, so I'll try that approach. What sort of attitude towards women does this type of game create? Attractive, half-dressed young women on screen together with monsters, and then they all have to be slaughtered.

Jason is at the age where he is starting to be interested in girls, is this the sort of image he should have of women?

As long as I don't get too upset. That would only defeat my aim. I'm not trying to prove that I'm right, proving a point for the sake of it is never the solution. I want to show them that this is pure evil in the form of a game.

Computer Games

Questions for Granddad's story

1 What were Granddad's good intentions for his visit and why couldn't he keep to them?

2 Would he still have found the game offensive if he wasn't a Christian?

3 Would it have been better if he'd explained to Jason and Michael why he was upset?

4 Do you think Granddad is exaggerating about how bad the game is?

5 Is it possible to justify a game that is just about shooting people to pieces?

Computer Games

Questions for both stories

1 Granddad talks about the game being Satanic. What does he mean by this, and is he right about the game?

2 Do you think that the boys' view of women might be affected by the game?

3 Granddad decides not to raise the subject of religion when discussing the game. Is this a good idea?

4 What is it about this kind of game that attracts people? Do you think that everyone is attracted by them?

5 Is there any point in banning everything that might possibly be seen as violent? Would there be anything left? (After all, even 'Bambi' shows animals being shot!)

6 Is the best solution to restrict access to games or films whose main focus is violence?

7 How do you feel about violent games and films?

Continued ...

8 Do you feel that such games and films affect people's behaviour?

9 What would be the best way for the family to discuss the subject? Do you think they need to?

10 Do you think Jocelyn will mind Granddad raising the subject with her? Might she already know about the game?

9 Staying the Night

Sonya's story

Sonya turned around at the door, "Bye," she shouted happily. "I'm going to Marcus's house."

"Bye," answered Mum and Dad. "Don't be too late."

"I won't," she answered without thinking. Then she stopped with her hand on the door.

"Actually, I'm staying the night so you don't need to wait up for me. Bye." She tried to rush out immediately but Dad got there first.

"Sonya, wait!"

"Yes, what do you want?" She tried to sound a bit bored and slightly annoyed, even though she knew exactly what it was about.

"Did you say you were staying the night at Marcus's house?"

"Yes, what's wrong with that? I've stayed the night at loads of my friends' houses ever since I was about six. Bye."

"Come back in the house Sonya, we need to talk about this." Dad didn't sound annoyed but he did sound determined, the way he always did when he felt it was time for a bit of parental guidance. (It didn't happen that often, but it was always a pain when it did.)

Sonya gave an exaggerated sigh, but she had no option so she flopped onto a chair in the kitchen.

She decided to go for a straightforward approach. She found that often parents understood things better when you spoke simply and clearly, as if you were talking to a child. Also, you shouldn't show that you feel hurt or disrespected, even if you do. It worked better if you could hide your emotions. She took a deep breath.

"It's Friday night and there's no school tomorrow, so Marcus and I thought we'd play a few CDs and chat and then tomorrow morning we've got band practice, so I thought it would be easier if I stayed the night. OK? Can I go now?"

There was a silence.

"You've got Marcus's number in case you miss me too much," she added with a little laugh.

She started to get up.

"Wait," said Mum. "Do his parents know that you're staying the night? Will they be at home?"

"Does it make any difference?" mumbled Dad.

"It does make a bit of a difference if there's going to be a responsible adult in the house," said Mum.

Sonya thought quickly, this was becoming a crisis. Marcus's parents were away, that was the whole point.

"She's only fifteen," said Dad annoyed. "She's too young to be staying at her boyfriend's house."

"What do you think we'll do?" she asked Dad a little scornfully. "As you say, we are only fifteen and we're not sleeping with each other if that's what you think."

It was true (not that it was any of their business) and it was also true that they didn't exactly intend to make love that night either. They might sleep in the same bed, and lie next to each other and might kiss and cuddle a bit, in fact they probably would.

Marcus was really nice; he would never pressure her into doing anything she didn't want to. (And anyway, if she did want to, well, that was another thing altogether.) At that moment, sitting at the kitchen table, the idea of them having sex together seemed a long way off but how could she explain that to her parents? Should it even be necessary for her to have to explain it to her parents?

"There's a first time for everything," said Dad. "And fifteen is far too young. I'm certain of that."

"All you adults can think about is sex!" shouted Sonya. "Marcus isn't like that, I know he wouldn't do anything I didn't want him to do."

"I believe you," said Dad. "But I'm not sure it makes me feel any better."

Sonya bit her lip.

"Will his parents be home or not?" repeated Mum.

93

"No," Sonya said tonelessly.

She didn't want to lie and anyway it would be too easy to check.

"In that case you'll spend the night here," said Mum decisively. "Be home by midnight at the latest, OK?"

"Well then, if Marcus and I did want to have sex, even though we don't, we'd still have time to do it anyway!" she shouted, "Before the last bus home. So what's the difference?"

"Be home by midnight," repeated Dad. "That's our final offer. Have a nice time."

Sonya slammed the front door and went to get the bus. She hated them. Surprisingly enough, she hated herself too, she felt as if she'd let herself be manipulated, but she couldn't quite work out how.

Staying the Night

Questions for Sonya's story

1 Why does Sonya get so angry? Has she let herself be manipulated?

2 Is it any of her parents' business what she and Marcus do when they're alone?

3 Marcus is gentle and kind and would never force Sonya to do anything she didn't want to, so Sonya thinks there won't be a problem. What do you think?

4 Does Sonya take the right approach when talking to her parents?

5 How could she have dealt with the issue differently?

9 Staying the Night

Mum's story

Sonya was on her way out, and just as she got to the door she said that she was going to spend the night at her boyfriend's house. She said it in passing, as if it was the most natural thing in the world.

"It was worth a try," thought Mum. I suppose I tried the same sort of thing when I was a teenager, but Sonya was stopped on the doorstep. Steaming with indignation she threw herself down at the kitchen table.

She made the idea of her staying at her boyfriend's house sound perfectly sensible. It was Friday night, there was no school tomorrow and she and Marcus had band practice the next morning. What could be more natural or convenient than her staying the night?

Mum wanted to know more, would his parents be home, for instance?

Sonya got annoyed. They weren't going to have sex together, if that's what they were thinking. And anyway, if that was what this was all about they'd have plenty of time to have sex before Sonya got the last bus home, so banning her from staying was completely pointless wasn't it?

Mum could see Sonya was getting really angry.

"Then maybe it would be best if you don't go over to see Marcus at all," she was tempted to say, but managed to bite her tongue. I must be very careful about what I say, she thought to herself. I could really spoil things

if I'm not careful. It's probably better if I let her and Dad argue with each other, they're used to it, sometimes it seems like they almost enjoy it.

Then she began to remember.

There was Sonya sitting at the other side of the kitchen table angry and getting hot in her coat which she refused to take off, but it could just as easily have been her 25 years ago.

Sonya looked older than fifteen, just as Mum had at that age. She was an innocent, beautiful young woman. Self-assured on the outside, bright and quick to lash out with her tongue. She could be really cutting, just like I used to be.

She'd had this sort of run-in with her own parents about sleeping over at her boyfriend's house. (He was called Robert and had red hair she remembered, and he laughed a lot. He was very kind and thoughtful.) Her parents had said absolutely not, and gone on about morals and the dangers of getting pregnant or catching diseases and about how easy it was for a girl to get a bad reputation. Told her she was far too young to be thinking of things like that.

She remembered how she had felt. That fantastic feeling of being in love with someone had been turned into something dirty. She loved Robert, but her parents thought that love and sex were the same thing, they didn't know anything about real love, but they still had the right to decide what she did. She had hated them because they had turned the best thing she'd ever had into something dirty.

I have to accept that Sonya's going to be angry with me, she thought, but she mustn't hate me like I hated my own mother back then.

Eventually she'd defied the ban and managed to sneak a night with Robert when he was at home on his own. She'd said she was staying with her best friend, who had covered for her. And of course they'd ended up having sex, even though that hadn't been her intention. No, he hadn't put her under pressure, perhaps she had even been the one who had taken the lead. Had she suffered because of it?

"Be honest now," she thought to herself. "Did I suffer because of that night?" She still couldn't really say 25 years on.

It had certainly been dreadful for a while afterwards when she thought she might be pregnant. They hadn't thought about contraception, it had all been so unplanned. As she had waited anxiously to find out, she had felt like she'd got mixed up in something that was too big for her to handle.

But the actual experience, that night with Robert, had she suffered because of that?

No, she didn't remember it like that, it hadn't been as fantastic as she'd anticipated, but it wasn't terrible. What had caused her to suffer was the fear of being pregnant and of being found out.

Unfortunately, not everyone is as nice as Robert was and it was almost four years before she slept with a boy again. Perhaps that was it, perhaps she had been too young the first time.

But this was about Sonya. Her message was absolutely clear, Mum don't spoil this and don't get involved in something you don't understand. If I want something I know where to find you but just don't interfere!

Mum knew it was important to give young people some trust and freedom, and that by trying to stop them growing up you were not really doing your job as a parent. She didn't want to make the same mistakes her own parents had by being too strict.

On the other hand she couldn't just close her eyes to what was going on. You can also fail in your job as a parent if you let go too soon. A fifteen-year-old isn't a child but they are not an adult either. She came to a decision.

She wasn't at all sure that it was the right one, but she had to make a decision and this was a compromise.

"Be home by midnight at the latest," she said kindly, but firmly. "Have a nice time."

Sonya tried to argue, but then she slammed the door shut and went for the bus.

Staying the Night

Questions for Mum's story

1 How do you think Sonya would react to Mum's story about Robert?

2 Do young couples think about contraception the first time they have sex? Should Mum have talked to Sonya about her options?

3 Can a boy make a girl go further than she wants to – without really understanding that he's doing it? Can a girl do the same to a boy?

4 Mum thinks her decision is a compromise. Do you see it as a compromise? Do you think Sonya does?

5 Do you think Sonya will come home at midnight?

Staying the Night

Questions for both stories

1 Do you recognise the tactics Sonya uses when talking to her parents? Is this the best approach?

2 Is it best to try to avoid conflict with your parents or can it sometimes be a good thing?

3 Do adults think of teenage relationships more in terms of sex and teenagers more in terms of love?

4 Should we assume that a fifteen-year-old will always suffer from having sex at a young age?

5 Should Mum have told Sonya about her own experiences? Would Sonya have listened?

6 Was Mum's decision a sensible one?

7 What would your solution have been if you were in Mum's position? What would your own parents do?

Continued …

8 Sometimes parents should trust their children and not get involved, and at other times they would be failing their children if they didn't. Can you think of examples of these different types of situation?

9 Will Sonya's feelings towards her parents have changed because of this argument?

10 After Jesus

Jackie's story

She really tried to understand why Edward didn't get it. After all, he was still young and quite immature. She tried to explain things compassionately and sincerely, but whatever she said to Edward she just couldn't get through.

"Jesus," she prayed. "Give me the right words. I want to be able to tell my son about the best thing that has ever happened to me, so that he understands." But she could hear for herself that the words were not enough.

"My whole life changed when I found Jesus," she said.

Edward refused to look up from his game.

"It was like coming from darkness into the light," she said, as she plucked up her courage and put her arm around his shoulder.

Edward's whole body stiffened as he turned away.

"Can't you see how different I am now?" she asked. "Can't you see that I'm sober every day and I have been for the past four years, ever since I found Jesus? Can't you see that there's food on the table when you come home and you don't need to go to Mrs Hunter asking for food because I'm high or drunk. You must see the difference and it's all because Jesus saved me."

Edward stood up and walked out.

After Jesus, she loved Edward more than anything in the world.

It was for his sake that she worked and slaved all the hours of the day. Sometimes she was so tired she just wanted to die and go home to Jesus. In Heaven you never feel worn out, but she brushed such thoughts away, she and Jesus brushed them away together.

"Edward needs a mother. Your job is to be a good mother to Edward," Jesus had told her and he sounded really firm.

She nodded in agreement.

"Yes, I want to do that, I do love Edward. Next to you there's no-one I love more than Edward, but I do get so tired sometimes."

"Yes, you do," Jesus said. "But you must never forget that I will give you the strength you need."

She never forgot.

She laughed out loud to herself. How could she be anything but happy when Jesus lived in her heart and she had his love?

"I know that you love me Jesus," she said. And she felt his love through her whole body and felt comforted.

She would have been completely happy if only Edward shared her joy. She understood that talking about beliefs could sound too much to people who did not have their own faith. If nothing else, Edward must be able to see the change in her. Couldn't he see the change?

A drunken, drug-taking wreck of a person had changed and could stand up and look people in the eye again. She'd stopped all the drugs, she'd even stopped smoking, and had stopped bringing men home. First she started out delivering leaflets, and then she'd got the job in the supermarket. (It had been a big drop in income, but what difference does money make when you have self-respect?) For the first time since Edward was born she'd been able to function as a proper mother who was really looking after her child.

At the very last minute, when the social workers had started to threaten to take Edward into care she had managed to change.

"Thank you Jesus," she whispered. "Now I can look the social workers in the eye and say, I'm not the person I was, I'm a Christian and Edward's mother!"

Of course, no-one had believed her at first, which wasn't really surprising after the way she'd been but now she had a new approach to life and it showed. When they came to visit the flat was clean and tidy and a real home, and she and Edward were clean and well dressed. She was always sober and she never asked people for money any more.

"I can look after myself and my son now. I've been saved!"

That's how she'd been able to keep Edward, it was a miracle. She'd eventually been able to keep her son even though the foster home had been all arranged.

It must have been the work of God.

105

After Jesus

Questions for Jackie's story

1 What does faith mean to Jackie?

2 Has finding faith been a good or bad thing for her?

3 Why does Jackie find it hard to understand Edward's feelings?

4 Why does Edward ignore her and walk away?

5 Does Jackie want Edward to find faith for his sake or for hers?

10 After Jesus

Edward's story

In Edward's life there was the time Before Jesus and the time After Jesus. The time after Jesus started after his Mum found Jesus about four years ago. He was only nine at the time but he still remembered.

Things were different after that.

She'd stopped drinking and there'd been food in the house every day. There was no more fighting and screaming and no more men, who always wanted to be called Dad when they were drunk, who stayed for a while and then disappeared again. Since his Mum had found Jesus there had only been her and Edward, so in that way it was really good.

Not everything had been bad before though.

Mrs Hunter from next door had been kind. She always gave him food when he was hungry and sometimes she even let him sleep there. There had been lots of different reasons why he preferred it to sleeping at home. And Mrs Hunter had a dog that he took out for walks, so some things had been good then too.

Then Jesus came.

At first Edward just thought she was in love with a new man, and in a way she was. Except this time you couldn't see him. He was a religious man

107

who'd lived a long, long time ago but still seemed to be with them every minute of the day and night. He was Mum's big new love and she didn't get over it. That was the problem, she didn't get over him like she had with all the other men. It seemed to him that Jesus took what he needed from Mum and Edward got what was left, which wasn't much.

The worst thing was that Jesus interfered with everything.

It would have been OK if he'd just interfered with Mum's life. She didn't seem to mind it, but he always seemed to interfere in Edward's life too.

It was quite strange how someone who lived thousands of years ago and was completely invisible could still do so much interfering. But it happened.

Everything that Jesus didn't like was called a sin.

That seemed to cover everything that was fun. It was a sin to read certain books, it was a sin to meet girls unless they were members of the church. It was a sin to do anything cool on a Sunday. It was a sin to have a tattoo even though it was just done with pen and it was a sin to have cool clothes. It was a sin to go to the cinema, or at least it was if it was a good film.

Edward wondered how his Mum could know what Jesus thought was a sin.

"It's in the Bible," she said.

"And where does is say in the Bible that we shouldn't go to the cinema?" he asked. "That's just stupid."

"It says in the Bible that violence is a sin, but you can ask the vicar, he knows more about it than I do," Mum had said.

It was the vicar and that church who were putting these ideas into her head. The vicar made up what Jesus thought, Edward was sure of it. When he said this to his Mum she was angry at first which was OK, but then she got upset and that was worse.

"Edward," she had cried, putting her arms around him. "You have to let Jesus into your heart. It's the only thing that's important, can't you see?" Then she'd pushed him down onto his knees and she knelt next to him in front of the picture of Jesus she had on the wall. She's started going on about how Edward should open his heart to Jesus. But first Edward must want it for himself.

Edward closed his lips. He didn't want Jesus to come into his heart. What would happen if he said it? He didn't really know, probably just that his Mum would be happy, which would be good.

But what if Jesus did exist after all? Edward would never get any peace. There'd be someone there all the time nagging him and saying that everything that was fun was a sin, so Edward kept his mouth shut tight.

At times like this he missed how his Mum was before Jesus, however bad it sometimes seemed. At least then Edward wasn't just the one she liked second-best after Jesus.

After Jesus

Questions for Edward's story

1 Do you think things were better for Edward before or after his Mum found Jesus?

2 Should Edward do as his Mum says if it would make her happy?

3 Would Edward feel happier?

4 Could Edward tell his Mum how he feels?

5 Is there anyone else Edward could talk to about this?

After Jesus

Questions for both stories

1 Jackie feels that religion was the only reason she sorted out her life and was able to keep Edward, can she make him understand how important this is for her?

2 Edward feels jealous and that he comes second to Jesus in his Mum's life. Is he right? Can his Mum help him with how he feels?

3 Why does Jackie stay with a church that tells her everything is a sin?

4 Is it wrong of Edward not to do what his Mum wants or is it wrong of his Mum to try to force him?

5 Can you make a decision to believe in something or is it something that just happens to you?

6 What might happen if Jackie took her faith a little less seriously?

7 Could Edward be a little more understanding about his Mum's beliefs?

8 Both Jackie and Edward would like to have a better life together How might they achieve it?

11　White Lies & Black Truths

Megan's story

It was an old pop song from the 1980s and it was really good fun to sing. It went on for ever and ever, and the chorus got longer and longer after every verse and it drove you mad. That was the whole idea. They had sung it on the way to the school trip until the teachers had almost gone insane and on the bus home again too. It was an awful, wonderful song.

Now there was going to be a talent show to raise funds for the school. Everyone was going to join in. Megan hadn't signed up at first because she wasn't very keen on performing, but at the same time she had quite enjoyed singing the song.

Her friend Ashley, who was signing people up for the show, had talked Megan into it. She knew that Megan was really nervous but at the same time she wanted to do it, and Ashley could be very persuasive. Megan said that she would sing a pop song but she hadn't said which one, it was going to be a surprise. Every time she thought about it she felt sick with nerves but she made herself think positively. Of course it would work, it had been great fun on the bus.

Today was the day.

Her legs were shaking when she went forward to the microphone. "And now Megan is going to sing a mystery song!" announced Ashley.

She began to sing without any accompaniment. At first people listened politely but she was so nervous there wasn't much to listen to, her voice could hardly be heard and she kept having to stop and swallow, but she soldiered on.

If only the song would come to an end! But it never did of course, that was the whole point. The song would go on and on until it drove everyone crazy.

The thing was that the audience didn't seem to understand and in the end they stopped listening. At first people started whispering to each other and then the talking got louder and some people started to get up to go to the toilet or buy a drink. Megan just kept on singing and singing. She was getting more and more confused but she kept on singing until at last she finished. Holding back her tears she gave the microphone back to Ashley and rushed off to the canteen to console herself. No-one really clapped, and some people were even laughing – she felt like she had made a total fool of herself!

After a while she began to feel better. At least some people had clapped, and probably more than she had realised, she had just been too nervous to notice. She'd kept on singing even though she was really nervous, which was good and now it was over and she was beginning to feel fine. Of course, she had to admit it could have been better, she hadn't exactly brought the house down, but what did they expect – it wasn't a TV show. She had quite a good voice and was good at singing. It wasn't the best she'd ever done, but it was OK and it was easy to be critical of yourself when you were feeling nervous. After all, the song was great fun, wasn't it?

She had just about convinced herself that her performance had been OK when her best friend Lauren turned up. Megan smiled at her.

"I'm so glad that's over," she laughed. "What did you think?"

Lauren didn't say anything.

"I was so nervous," continued Megan. "But at least I kept going and it is a good song isn't it?"

Lauren still didn't say anything and warning bells started to go off in Megan's head. "Don't say any more, change the subject now," she thought. But what was a best friend for, if not this kind of thing?

"Tell me truthfully, what did you think?" she repeated.

"Do you really want me to?" asked Lauren.

"Yes, of course I do. It would be good to know that it was OK and that it wasn't a total disaster," she said nervously.

"But it was," said Lauren dryly, and then she explained why.

Megan just wanted to die.

She couldn't show how upset she was because after all she had asked for an honest answer. So she pretended to accept all the negative criticism, although it was racing round and round in her head. She nodded and said she wasn't upset, definitely not.

But really all she wanted to do was run away and hide.

White Lies & Black Truths

Questions for Megan's story

1 Why did Megan ask Lauren what she thought?

2 Megan was upset when she first left the stage but then began to feel alright, is it easy to convince yourself that something has turned out OK after all?

3 Was Lauren being unkind?

4 Could she have said something else without actually lying?

5 How will Megan feel in front of everyone at school now?

11 White Lies & Black Truths

Lauren's story

Lauren was a bit annoyed with Megan.

Ever since Megan had decided to sing in the talent show she could hardly talk about anything else and at the same time she was being so secretive. She wouldn't say what she was going to sing, only that it was an eighties song, and then she'd giggle.

"You'll hear it on the night of the show, then you can tell me the truth about what you think of it."

Lauren was going to take part as well, admittedly with four other girls, but she was still taking part. They were going to mime and dance to a well-known song and that wasn't easy to do as a group. It wasn't just that they had to mime in perfect synchronisation to the music, they also needed to be synchronised with each other. The five girls had to be smooth and sexy and move together as one, and they practiced their dance routine over and over again. Megan wasn't interested in hearing about any of that though, she was too caught up in her own secret plans.

The day of the talent show arrived.

Lauren's group was on at the beginning of the programme. She was really nervous but it all went well. The audience was in good spirits and cheered and clapped.

"What did you think? Tell me the truth," she whispered to Megan as soon as she came off the stage.

"Quite good, I think," Megan whispered back. "I'm so nervous I could die, so I wasn't really concentrating. It looked fine though."

Self-absorbed as usual!

After a while it was Megan's turn. Lauren really wanted to like what she heard, for Megan's sake. They were best friends after all and Megan had really got everyone's hopes up by being so secretive. It would feel good to be able to say it was excellent and mean it. It was almost as if the better the song was, the easier it would be to forgive Megan for being so full of herself.

But it wasn't good at all, it wasn't even not bad, it was completely awful!

Megan was singing without any music. Singing solo is brave enough, but to do it without music as well! That took some skill – one single voice taking on the whole audience. Megan would have needed to sing so well that there was total silence in the room, otherwise it could only be a disaster.

But Megan couldn't even sing in tune. If the song had a tune she kept it to herself.

It was obvious how nervous she was. She stopped over and over again, swallowed and then stumbled on. It was painfully embarrassing to listen to and to watch.

The words, when you could hear them, were repetitive and pointless, just a jumble of unconnected words that never ended. The audience started getting restless, would she ever finish so that they could get rid of her? This was painful, but she carried on! That was the worst part, she just went on and on singing that never-ending jumble of words in a toneless voice. People started talking to each other and leaving their seats as if the talent show had ended, and the only person who hadn't noticed was Megan, who just sang and sang.

They met afterwards in the canteen.

Lauren just wanted to avoid her but Megan was smiling at her.

"I'm so glad that's over," she laughed. "What did you think?"

Lauren was completely silent.

Was she mad? Did she expect praise? Didn't she realise how painfully embarrassing it had been?

"I was really nervous," Megan babbled on happily. "But I managed it anyway. Don't you think it's such a cool song?"

Lauren was no stranger to telling white lies when they were called for, and if Megan hadn't been so secretive and hadn't been completely useless then perhaps she might have said something vague about it not being too bad.

She just kept quiet because she didn't know what to say.

"What did you think?" Megan went on. "Tell me honestly."

Lauren got quite angry.

"Do you want me to?" she asked.

"Yes, of course I do, it would be good to know if it was OK and that it wasn't a total disaster," Megan laughed in a self-satisfied way.

"But it was," said Lauren and then she explained, very clearly, why.

She wondered if she'd been a bit harsh. She would much rather have comforted Megan, that's for sure, but her lack of awareness and self-satisfaction were just too much.

She had to tell Megan the truth, it was for her own good, but it didn't seem that she was taking any notice.

She pretended to be listening but could she have heard? Megan just said that she was glad Lauren had told her the truth, as that's what she'd asked her to do and that it hadn't bothered her at all.

But was she being honest? Some people were just so full of themselves that nothing got through to them.

White Lies & Black Truths

Questions for Lauren's story

1 Why was Lauren so annoyed with Megan?

2 Why did Megan ask Lauren what she thought?

3 Was Lauren being deliberately unkind?

4 Are there situations where the truth should sometimes be told, even though it might cause hurt? Was this one of those occasions?

5 Do you think Megan will take in Lauren's criticism? What do you think she's thinking?

White Lies & Black Truths

Questions for both stories

1 Why did the song work so well on the bus?

2 Megan re-invents the truth to make herself feel better. Is it wrong to do this?

3 It's never really that bad to fail at something, but how can you admit it to yourself and cope with it afterwards?

4 Why is Lauren angry with Megan?

5 It seems that Lauren is embarrassed on Megan's behalf. Does she need to be? Why is she?

6 Is Lauren just being mean when she gives such harsh criticism?

7 Why doesn't Megan show Lauren how upset she is?

Continued …

8 What would Lauren have said to Megan if she'd been a really good friend?

9 Do you think that Megan was self-absorbed?

10 Is there a place in life for 'white lies'? Even between true friends?

123

12 Beach-Stone Battalions

Jay's story

Brothers, thought Jay, they were either too old or too young. Why couldn't they be just the right age? His age!

Jay thought he had the answer, at least in theory.

There was only one way to change things and that was through science. Through science it should be possible to solve the problem with a practical solution. All children could be born two at a time, like twins. That would mean everyone would have someone of their own age to be with.

In that case Tom would be Jay's twin but he'd be thirteen like Jay not fifteen. What about Hari who was only eight? That was something to think about.

Did they really need him? He could be quite cute and he couldn't help being young. He would have to have a twin too, so that he wouldn't be hanging round Jay's neck all the time.

At the moment life seemed unusually good. They were all away on a family holiday and there wasn't a friend of Tom's in sight. (His friends always laid claim to him otherwise.)

All three brothers were having a really good time together.

Seeing Through the Eyes of Another, L. Collmar, 2010 **125**

Tom had invented the Beach-Stone Battalions, numbers 1 to 6. Jay was Battalion 1 and Hari was Battalion 6, Battalions 2 to 5 didn't exist but Tom said it sounded much more impressive with six. Tom was Commander-in-Chief.

The game had started the day before when they'd gone for a walk. The beaches were more pebbles than sand and the ground was covered in them so they'd started a pebble war, throwing them into the sea, which was great fun. Then Tom had decided that they were the Beach-Stone Battalions on a secret mission and the game got even better. They were the Beach-Stone people and spoke in weird voices. Tom was the one who decided on the voices. He was so good at imaginary games but he hardly ever played these days. He was almost like a grown up and was really boring when he was with his friends.

But not now though, not when he was Commander-in-Chief. Hari was included in the game too, but it was just a shame that his aim was so bad and he got very upset when Tom and Jay both decided to aim at him.

"Ow!" he cried. "That was really hard, right in the middle of my head. It hurt!" He began to cry and ran home to Mum.

The Beach-Stone Battalions had needed an enemy so they invented the Pebble Patrol, which was Hari. They hadn't meant to be horrible to him, but if you're in a stone war then you throw stones, it's as simple as that, and he had wanted to be part of it after all.

When they got back to the cottage Tom sat down at the computer.

He messed around for a while and suddenly they could record onto the computer's microphone. They sang Beach-Stone songs. Tom was a strict director, he wasn't happy until a song was perfect and everything was just as he wanted it. They sang in their weird voices and then Tom played the songs back in double time so they sounds like mad excited mice. They laughed till they cried.

Hari joined in too. He'd forgiven them ages ago and so they let him join in as long as he didn't talk while they were recording and didn't touch anything.

All afternoon and late into the evening they sat at the computer recording different songs. They recorded silly versions of all sorts of songs. None of them were the Beach-Stone national anthem though. Jay wrote the words and music to a special national anthem which they all sang before they went into battle. When they had eight songs finished on the computer Tom burned them onto a CD and gave it to Jay.

The Beach-Stone Battalions were great fun, but things weren't always such great fun with his brothers. Usually they were either too old or too young. Twins would be perfect. He decided he'd be a scientist when he was older and fix the problem for himself.

Beach-Stone Battalions

Questions for Jay's story

1 Would life be better if everyone had a twin?

2 How does it feel when you can't spend as much time as you want with older brothers or sisters?

3 Do brothers and sisters become more like strangers when they get older?

4 Can you have more fun with older or younger brothers and sisters?

5 Tom seems to enjoy playing silly games but only when his friends aren't around. Is that how people get when they get a bit older?

12 Beach-Stone Battalions

Hari's story

It was fun on holiday. Mum had rented a cottage for a couple of weeks at the end of the summer holiday and they all had a fantastic time.

For the first time ever, Hari had been given homework to do over the holidays. He had to write a diary about what he'd done during the holidays. They had to write a diary and do drawings and stick things in to remind themselves of what they'd done and seen.

"Jay and Tom and I had a beach stone war," he was going to write and then he was going to do a drawing of it. Underneath he planned to stick a stone. He laughed to himself, he'd never be able to close the book properly, the stone would be far too big, but he'd still decided to include it anyway.

The best thing about the cottage was that he'd been able to play with Jay and also with Tom, his oldest brother. That was because there was no-one else around. Tom was so old that he'd almost stopped playing altogether. He was fifteen. Jay was also quite old, he was thirteen, but at least he could still play. He didn't play with Hari very often though, he was too little. It seemed that his brothers were getting older and older but he was always going to be eight.

Now every day was fun.

"We've been so lucky with the weather," Mum would say every morning as the sun continued to shine and the sea seemed to get warmer.

The brothers had composed the Beach-Stone national anthem. Jay had thought of it, and written both the words and the music. Jay was great at things like that.

The beach was covered in pebbles and stones. That was the best thing about it all, there were so many stones to have a war with and none of Jay's or Tom's friends as far as the eye could see. It was the perfect holiday spot.

It was Tom's idea to put them into Beach-Stone Battalions and he was Commander-in-Chief. Hari didn't really understand everything, but that didn't matter. Jay was Battalion 1 and he was Battalion 6. There were no more Battalions even though he thought there should be numbers 2, 3, 4 and 5 as well.

"Yes," said Tom. "There should be, but it sounds more impressive like this."

Hari still didn't really understand, but the main thing was that he was allowed to join in.

Sometimes though, he couldn't understand why Tom changed all the rules he had made just when he felt like it. First he decided that Hari should be Beach-Stone Battalion 6 but then suddenly he had to be the Pebble Patrol which was the Beach-Stone Battalions' enemy. Before he knew it Tom and Jay were both attacking him, and that wasn't much fun at all.

Hari tried not to mind but they were throwing so hard it wasn't easy. The last straw was when they hit him so hard on the head that it was almost bleeding. Well, it wasn't exactly bleeding but it left a red mark and it hurt so much he started to cry even though he tried not to.

He wanted to be one of the Beach-Stone Battalions because they were best, that's what they kept singing. He didn't want to be the enemy. And he began to cry. He felt so ashamed that he ran home. I'm not old enough he thought, I can't join in with this either. I don't want to be a stupid Pebble just because I'm eight.

Later everything was good again. Tom suggested that they record all the Beach-Stone songs on the computer, so they sang in silly voices to make it sound really funny. They sang the Beach-Stone national anthem and lots of other Beach-Stone versions of real songs. Then Tom played them at double speed and they sounded even squeakier. He burned a CD with all the songs on it and it worked. They had their own CD and Jay was going to look after it even though it belonged to all of them.

Hari thought about it all for a while.

It was great fun to play with Jay and Tom as long as he could join in properly and didn't have to be a Pebble, but it didn't happen very often. Most of the time he went around just wishing he could play with Jay and Jay went around wishing he could play with Tom and Tom probably went around wishing he could be with some girl or other in town. (That's what Hari thought anyway.) The girl probably wished she could be with someone completely different.

Beach-Stone Battalions

Questions for Hari's story

1 Are the older boys deliberately unkind to Hari?

2 Why does Hari want to spend so much time with his older brothers?

3 Should you expect to be included if you are so much younger than your brothers or sisters?

4 What makes the older boys happy to play on holiday when they don't at home?

5 Should Hari just be pleased he is allowed to join in?

Beach-Stone Battalions

Questions for both stories

1 What does it feel like to have a younger person following you round all the time?

2 How does it feel not to be allowed to join in just because you're too young?

3 Can young people have fun together despite age differences? Can adults?

4 Are things more fun when you are with older siblings or younger ones?

5 Is it better to have a brother or sister who can be annoying than to be an only child?

6 Tom seems to like behaving quite childishly for a change, can this be fun sometimes?

7 Is it more fun to be with your brothers and sisters or with friends of your own age?

Continued …

8 Is seems that one person always has to be left out of a group, why might this be?

9 Can you have more fun with brothers and sisters when there are no other friends around?

13 The Lizard's Heritage

Jane's story

Jane sat at her desk and dreamt. At the moment it was Citizenship, and they were doing human rights, of course, they always seemed to with The Lizard.

Their teacher been named 'The Lizard' a long time ago and the name had been passed down through the school. It had been given because she always said: "I know you think I'm an old dinosaur but ..." and inevitably along would come a long lecture on the importance human rights and morals to people's lives.

At first she'd been called 'The Dinosaur', then it was shortened to 'Dino' but that sounded too cute, so it was changed again and then she became 'The Lizard'. For The Lizard, Citizenship meant human rights and strong morals.

She would start by saying that we should appreciate that we all have certain freedoms and then would add that no matter what people believed in they should know that citizenship is underpinned by a system of values, rights and morals. If you wanted to learn anything about history, politics or even music and literature then you needed to know about human rights and responsibilities, and most of all morals.

The first time she said this Jane thought it sounded really interesting but after the hundredth time it became a huge bore.

"The Lizard's heritage," someone would whisper every time she said it and people who could be bothered giggled.

Even though The Lizard was standing at the front of the class it wasn't her Jane was thinking about. She was thinking about whether or not she should go to the anti-globalisation demonstration in London and also whether she still wanted to be with Louis. A whole gang of them had planned to go, Louis included. If she decided to go then she'd have to have a huge row with Mum and Dad, which she could put up with, but would the trip really be worth it? She wasn't sure any more.

She sympathised with the demonstrators, she knew what she thought about globalisation and didn't think that all the power and wealth in the world should be held by just a few old men. That wasn't true equality, but she didn't like the idea that the demonstrations often ended in riots. A few people always seemed to take over and started breaking car windows or setting fire to things and throwing stones at the police. She knew she didn't like that sort of thing. That type of person didn't care about human rights or democracy or globalisation, it didn't matter to them what the demonstration was about, whether it was for something or against it, it was all the same to them – just an opportunity for a fight.

It seemed to her that sometimes the police felt the same way too, whatever a demonstration was about it didn't matter as long as they got to fight. She certainly didn't want to be mistreated by the police just because she wanted to express an opinion.

Why did it always have to be like that, with stupidity and violence seeming to take over with both the demonstrators and the police? Why didn't people listen to each other? Was there any point at all in engaging in these sorts of events? She just didn't know any more. Just as she didn't know any more whether it was such a great idea to go away with Louis for four days. Why were things so difficult? It didn't matter whether the subject was politics or relationships, they both meant getting involved.

The Lizard's voice broke into her thoughts.

"Jane! I asked you a question."

"It's all based on morals and responsibility," said Jane automatically.

"What do you mean, haven't you been listening?" asked The Lizard, annoyed.

"Err, no, I mean yes," said Jane hastily.

"Don't you care about human rights at all?"

"Of course I do."

"Well, make an effort to listen then."

The Lizard gave a sigh and started to repeat the same old stuff about the priceless human rights that are at the root of our society and which underpin democracy. She then ended by saying that while she understood that there was a lot going on in our teenage bodies, it should still be possible to have a few thoughts from time to time about important things like rights and democracy, and not be totally sluggish and indifferent.

Of course, she might have mentioned the answer to her question too, but by that time Jane had already stopped listening again so she never did find out.

The Lizard's Heritage

Questions for Jane's story

1 Is the Lizard right, should everyone learn about the rights and morals underpinning society? If so, why doesn't Jane listen?

2 Is Jane really as sluggish and indifferent as the Lizard suggests?

3 Why does Jane feel that she might not go to the demonstration? Is it because she doesn't care about the issues?

4 Can Jane relate what The Lizard is saying to her own thoughts?

5 How could The Lizard make things more relevant to Jane and the rest of the class?

13 The Lizard's Heritage

The Lizard's story

I can't help it, she thought, we all get our hobby horses over the years, you just can't help returning to a subject that's important to you. I'm sure all teachers do it. In fact, most people do, don't they?

She knew very well that as a teacher she put an emphasis on moral responsibility and human rights. She couldn't deny how strongly she felt about these things, but what was wrong with being passionate about your subject?

She wasn't out to try to make them all into perfect citizens. If her students wanted to base their lives on a strong moral code that was their business, but it was her job to ensure that they had an understanding of basic human rights and responsibilities. It was impossible to understand anything about history or politics or even literature if you didn't have an understanding of human rights.

She wanted to teach them the history of human rights, the different struggles through the ages against oppression that all lead to the freedoms in society today, and those struggles were grounded in moral responsibility.

Often, that history involved people taking charge of their own lives in the face of opposition, and the strong morals and will of a few had helped the many. To her the story had a personal connection. She had been no older than these children when she had found the courage to break away from her parents and follow a life she believed in.

Her domineering and old-fashioned parents had tried to steer her thoughts and feelings and the course of her life, but she had taken courage and left the security of home to go out into the unknown wider world. For a time she didn't have much money or even food, but good people had helped her.

How could these young people think she was just an old dusty dinosaur? She still believed in freedom just as much as they did, or perhaps even more so because of what it had cost her to go out on her own. There was no way of knowing the cost of such a move beforehand. How could you?

It's probably best that way, she thought, because if you knew the price you'd have to pay perhaps you would never follow your beliefs. But it is always worth the price. Always.

She had supported herself through college, and had become a teacher.

Over the years there had been many changes to the teaching profession, but she had always tried to stick to her moral code and her values. She had tried to show her students that life can be very poor without respect for others. The headmaster had called her an 'great enthusiast' at her sixtieth birthday party. Yes, she was, she really believed in the things she taught. She took great pleasure in giving young people access to knowledge. Knowledge was a priceless tool for the journey through life. She was simply doing her duty.

A class was like a living organism that you could connect to and work with. At other times when she had connected with classes it had been wonderful and they had developed a respect for each other.

In the past few years though things had changed.

She couldn't exactly put her finger on it, but something important had changed in the attitude of students. It wasn't just that they had become less respectful, which of course they had, but that was part of being young and often the cheekiest ones are the best once you reach them. She'd learned that over the years. No, it was more that they had just switched off.

For her, youth meant curiosity and enthusiasm and a desire to conquer the world. It meant a desire to go out into the world and explore ideas and beliefs. Today's youth didn't want seem to want to do anything and seemed very happy just to sit in front of a television with a bag of crisps. They didn't think of protest and revolution, they didn't have daring and challenging thoughts. Protesting requires clear thoughts and beliefs and they just didn't seem to have any.

Look at Jane, she doesn't bother to listen in lessons and is always distracted. Is there anything she cares about apart from boys and makeup and when the next party will be?

"Don't you understand?" she wanted to plead with the class. "I want to help you so that you can be real people, not half-asleep and apathetic. I want to give you the tools and knowledge to help you think so that you can experience life to the full. Then you'll be able to choose your own path in life and I won't interfere, but first I need you to wake up!"

The Lizard's Heritage

Questions for the Lizard's story

1 Do all teachers have favourite themes that they return to? Is that wrong?

2 Should The Lizard prioritise morals and rights in the way she does?

3 Why does she feel so strongly about people's rights and freedom of choice?

4 How does The Lizard feel about Jane?

5 The Lizard believes that something has changed in the way students think over the past few years, is she right? What might have caused this change?

The Lizard's Heritage

Questions for both stories

1 What do Jane and The Lizard have against each other? In what ways are they right?

2 Would you call the Lizard old fashioned or modern in her outlook, is she quite radical? How does she see herself?

3 What does The Lizard mean when she talks about going out into the world?

4 Do young people today feel strongly about wanting to change things? Do you?

5 Is a class like a living organism that a teacher connects with as a whole? Why has The Lizard started to lose her connection with the class?

6 Jane feels disappointed because people don't seem to listen to each other. What might happen if she and The Lizard started listening to each other?

7 What effect has the nickname of 'The Lizard' had on the way the students view their teacher?

Continued ...

8 Does The Lizard try to find out how her students feel about people's rights? Would she be disappointed or surprised if she questioned them further?

9 How would Jane feel about The Lizard if she knew more about her background and personal struggle?

10 Do human rights and moral responsibility form the basis of our society as The Lizard believes?

14 The New Girl

Fin's story

The new girl wasn't pretty, that wouldn't have made him notice her, there were loads of pretty girls in the school. No, she wasn't pretty, instead she was amazingly beautiful. Even though she had a figure like a model she hid it under baggy, dull clothes. She never wore makeup and never did anything to show off her stunning beauty.

To look sexy you must have to want to be sexy, thought Fin philosophically. Looking like Cheryl Cole doesn't help if you shuffle around like an old woman, because that's what the new girl seemed to do. She did look like a young Cheryl Cole and it was hard to believe that she was only about fourteen, but she didn't really shuffle around like an old woman, she moved with a grace that took all the boys' breath away.

Fin still thought she seemed to shuffle around. Physically, she moved around gracefully but psychologically she shuffled around. It was as if an old woman was slopping around in the body of a super-model. She didn't seem to care how attractive she was, or perhaps she didn't realise. Fin didn't understand her and he couldn't stop thinking about her.

He plucked up courage and went over to her.

"Hey, Hippo, what's your name?" He didn't want her to think he was too impressed, so he tried to be really casual. He didn't want to start off with her having the upper hand. Things would be best if she joked back at him and said something like "If I'm a hippo then you must be an elephant", and then they could start talking. Fin knew how to talk to girls.

She just looked nervous.

"Svetlana," she said quietly.

"That sounds like a Russian name or something," said Fin.

"Yes," said Svetlana.

"Are you from Russia?" continued Fin.

"My Mum …" murmured Svetlana in a low attractive voice, and walked away.

"Fin got the push," laughed the other boys, who were quite happy to see him rejected.

"That's fine," said Fin. "I was just warming up."

Despite several serious attempts at chatting up Svetlana he had no luck. She just have one-word answers, never laughed and didn't even smile, not even when he cracked his best jokes. His street-wise jokey style just didn't seem to make any impression on her at all.

A few of the other boys had a go at trying to impress her as well, but everyone got the same response, which made him feel a bit better. Then Fin gave his expert opinion.

"She just doesn't like boys."

But everyone told him he was being stupid and his theory made no sense, as Svetlana was just as uncommunicative towards the girls. She was never actually unfriendly but she never asked anyone a question, she was just quiet, and said as little as possible. Perhaps she was shy, although that would be very unusual for someone with her looks. Nobody could work it out.

She wasn't afraid to talk in lessons, and she even seemed to suck up to the teachers sometimes, she always seemed to know the answer, whatever the question. She never gave any personal opinions, just showed how much she knew, and it was obvious that she was clever. Sometimes she sounded like a bored tour-guide reciting facts to an audience, not wanting to show just how bored she was. She never laughed, she only smiled politely but the smile never seemed to reach her eyes.

"Who does she think she is?" said Fin to the others. "She's just full of herself, miserable and boring." (No-one needed to know that Fin was still intrigued by her and strangely enough, the more she pushed him away the worse it got.)

For a while, everyone tried to include Svetlana in what was going on but she turned down all of their invitations, and never responded if someone tried to show an interest in her, so in the end they just gave up. If she wanted to be on her own they would let her. Fin was right, she was full of herself, miserable and boring. No-one bothered her or bullied her, they weren't a bad crowd, but after a while they all adopted Fin's nickname for her and she became known as 'Hippo'.

The New Girl

Questions for Fin's story

1 Why does everyone start calling her 'Hippo'?

2 Are Fin and the others being unkind to Svetlana?

3 Who is to blame for the way people end up treating her?

4 Are they right to leave her alone? Do they have any choice?

5 Why do you think Svetlana keeps herself to herself?

6 Do you think she's happier being apart from the group?

14 The New Girl

Svetlana's story

It wasn't her imagination, people really did seem to stare at her, it had started a few months ago, in the autumn.

Her Mum had died last spring, Svetlana had only known she was ill for a few months and then she was gone. Soon afterwards Svetlana and her Dad moved, that was at the end of the summer and it seemed to be around about that time that people had started to stare at her.

Why had people started staring at her as if she had two heads, when it was bad enough that she'd lost her mother? She missed not having her Mum around even more after that. She would have known why people were staring and would have been able to explain it. But she was dead! All Svetlana had left was a few photographs. Sometimes she talked to her Mum's photograph as if she was there in the room. Was that wrong?

"Mum, what's wrong with me?" she'd ask. "Why do people stare at me all the time?"

Sadly, she never got an answer, Mum just smiled out at her from the photograph with her clear blue eyes.

"You must understand the reason," they seemed to say. "Don't you understand?"

But she didn't understand.

Dad never had been as good at answering these sorts of questions as Mum had been, but she tried anyway.

"Why do you think people are staring at me?" she asked.

He'd looked at her seriously and then looked a bit afraid before he gave a strained little laugh.

"They probably just think you're pretty", he'd said. "You're growing to be just like your mother." She might have been imagining it, but she was sure he hadn't been able to look her in the eye when he said it.

It had started at the beginning of the summer.

She had grown a lot really quickly and in just a few months her whole body had changed. She'd changed from a tall, thin girl into a whole new person. All of her bony corners had become rounded and softer. She didn't know herself anymore. It was as if when her Mum died she'd started to turn into her. It was crazy.

At first she thought she looked pretty good. It was both scary and cool at the same time, after all, who didn't want to be attractive? Then she began to realise that she must look awful because everyone was staring at her, and she couldn't understand why. No-one ever said anything, they just stared and everyone seemed to know what was wrong except her.

The first day at her new school was dreadful.

Everyone just stared and then one boy came over to her, he was called Fin, she learned later.

"Hi Hippo," he said. "What's your name?"

She forced herself to say her name.

"Sounds like a Russian name," he said, in a superior way.

"My Mum ..." she said quietly, and then she ran off in a panic.

If her Mum had still been alive, she might have felt she could joke with him a bit for calling her a name, and if he'd stopped trying to show off she might have been able to explain that she was called Svetlana because her Mum had come from Russia and it was quite a popular name there.

She probably would have been able to do it, but now she couldn't even speak. She hid in the toilets, just put the seat down, sat down and closed her eyes tight. She'd made a fool of herself already, on her first day!

She sat there and rubbed her eyes, rocking back and forwards and pictured her mother's eyes looking at her.

"Do you understand yet?" the eyes seemed to be saying. "Do you understand why everyone is staring?"

She did understand, he'd called her a hippo and it was true, she'd changed into a fat wobbling hippopotamus, she just hadn't realised because she hadn't let herself. She'd been too much of a coward. She should really be grateful to the boy who'd said it, she had wanted to know why people were staring and now she knew. What should she do now? Nothing, just bite her tongue and try to stand out as little as possible. If anyone spoke to her of course she would answer politely, but who'd want to talk to a hippo?

Only someone who wanted to tease her! If she kept her head down, maybe they'd lose interest in her.

It worked quite well, she managed to keep people at a distance and eventually they left her in peace. They still called her 'Hippo' but that was the way it should be, after all she was one and that's why people stared at her. Thanks Mum, for helping me understand she whispered to the photograph.

The New Girl

Questions for Svetlana's story

1 Do you think that everyone is really staring at Svetlana?

2 Why did Dad look afraid when she asked him questions?

3 What do you think Fin expects when he approaches Svetlana?

4 Why does Svetlana run away when Fin talks to her?

5 Why does Svetlana start to feel so different?

6 Has Svetlana chosen the best method for surviving in her new school? Is there anything else she could do?

The New Girl

Questions for both stories

1 Do you think people are staring at Svetlana? If so, why?

2 Why couldn't Svetlana's Dad look her in the eye when she spoke to him?

3 Fin's approach is relaxed and friendly, shouldn't Svetlana have realised this?

4 Is it Fin's fault that Svetlana thinks she looks like a hippo?

5 What would happen if someone tried to take the time to find out about the real Svetlana?

6 Can Svetlana really believe she's ugly?

7 How is it possible for someone to have such a misunderstanding of their own appearance?

Continued ...

8 Why does Svetlana talk to her Mum's photograph?

9 The class and Svetlana have really misunderstood each other, how might this be sorted out for the better?

10 What is Svetlana's main problem? What could be done to help her?

155

Also in this series:

Walking in the Shoes of Another
Lars Collmar
Translated by Lesley Gleeson

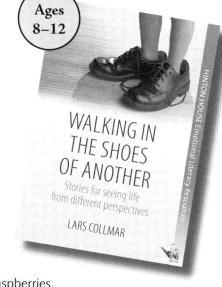

Ages
8–12

'Do not judge another until you have walked a mile in his moccasins.'
Native American Proverb

The stories in this volume are intended to encourage younger children to try seeing the events that happen around them from different perspectives and to try to understand other people's emotions.

Ten stories are told from two different perspectives. Events that might seem unfair, strange or untrue can appear completely different when seen from the viewpoint of someone else.

♦ When an old lady encourages two young boys to help themselves to her raspberries, why does she then get upset when there are none left?
♦ Why would a little boy be so thoughtless that he gets chocolate on his classmate's new dress?
♦ When mum and dad separate, should their daughter have to decide who is to blame?
♦ A boy is wrongly accused of shoplifting, why might the shopkeeper act as he does?

2010 ♦ 140pp ♦ A4 photocopiable paperback ♦ ISBN 978-1-906531-24-9

The Communication Toolkit
Assessing and Developing Social Communication Skills in Children and Adolescents
Belinda Medhurst

The Communication Toolkit is a practical collection of user-friendly resources designed to support young people aged 8 to 16 who have social and communication difficulties. It draws on a variety of theoretical backgrounds including emotional literacy, solution-focused and social-use-of-language approaches.

The accessible, photocopiable worksheets cover subjects such as self-concept & self-esteem, body language & facial expressions, awareness of self and others, relationship skills, conversational & listening skills, feeling safe and staying in control.

Through structured activities youngsters will be helped to develop emotional literacy, self-esteem, social understanding and ultimately behaviour and communication skills.

A varied and appealing resource that teachers, SLTs, SENCOs, psychologists and behaviour support workers will find invaluable for use with an older age group not always addressed in social skills materials.

2009 ♦ 206pp ♦ A4 photocopiable paperback ♦ ISBN 978-1-906531-26-3

info@hintonpublishers.com • www.hintonpublishers.com